"Just what the trauma field needed at just the right time. This book is 100% Brian Miller—clever, wise, articulate, and full of sage and nuanced advice for addressing secondary traumatic stress symptoms in real time. The model he offers is erudite, empowering, and hopeful. If I were curating a greatest hits list in professional literature, this would be top of the charts! I recommend a copy for yourself and another to share with students, supervisees, and colleagues".

Ginny Sprang, *PhD, professor of psychiatry, University of Kentucky, and executive director, Center on Trauma and Children*

"*Reducing Secondary Traumatic Stress* addresses one of the most pressing and currently unmet needs in the trauma field—the sustained wellness of providers. Drawing from personal stories, relatable examples, and empirical evidence, Dr. Miller provides concrete, practical strategies that anyone can add to their own practice. The importance of evidence-informed, effective strategies to address secondary trauma cannot be overstated, which is why I recommend this book and the CE-CERT model to anyone doing trauma work".

Megan Clarke, *MPH, National Center for Child Traumatic Stress, Duke University Medical Center*

"In *Reducing Secondary Traumatic Stress*, Miller has synthesized and distilled research from a wide range of fields to provide a roadmap for trauma-affected professionals to not just sustain their careers but to thrive in them! Going beyond the usual focus on self-care and work–life balance, Miller's CE-CERT model provides a discrete set of concrete skills and practices that empower professionals to consciously and systematically transform the risk of trauma work into a truly rewarding and affirming experience".

Brian E. Bride, *PhD, MSW, MPH, former editor-in-chief of* Traumatology *and Distinguished University Professor and director of the School of Social Work at Georgia State University*

Reducing Secondary Traumatic Stress

Reducing Secondary Traumatic Stress presents a model for supporting emotional well-being in workers who are exposed to the effects of secondary trauma. The book provides helping professionals with a portfolio of skills that supports emotion regulation and recovery from secondary trauma exposure and also that enhances the experience of the helping encounter. Each chapter presents evidence-informed skills that allow readers to regulate distressing emotions and to foster increased empathy for those suffering from trauma. *Reducing Secondary Traumatic Stress* goes beyond the usual discussion of burnout to talk in specific terms about what we do about the very real stress that is produced by this work.

Brian C. Miller, PhD, has experience in a variety of behavioral health direct practice, clinical leadership, and policy roles. He holds a PhD from Case Western Reserve in Cleveland, Ohio.

Reducing Secondary Traumatic Stress

Skills for Sustaining a Career in the Helping Professions

Brian C. Miller

Routledge
Taylor & Francis Group

NEW YORK AND LONDON

First published 2022
by Routledge
605 Third Avenue, New York, NY 10158

and by Routledge
2 Park Square, Milton Park, Abingdon, Oxon, OX14 4RN

Routledge is an imprint of the Taylor & Francis Group, an informa business.

Library of Congress Cataloging-in-Publication Data

Names: Miller, Brian C., 1956- author.
Title: Reducing secondary traumatic stress: skills for sustaining a career in the helping professions / Brian C. Miller.
Description: New York: Routledge, 2021. | Includes bibliographical references and index.
Identifiers: LCCN 2021001539 (print) | LCCN 2021001540 (ebook) | ISBN 9780367494582 (hardback) | ISBN 9780367494575 (paperback) | ISBN 9781003049043 (ebook)
Subjects: LCSH: Medical personnel--Job stress. | Secondary traumatic stress--Treatment. | Burn out (Psychology)--Treatment.
Classification: LCC RC451.4.M44 M55 2021 (print) | LCC RC451.4.M44 (ebook) | DDC 610.69--dc23
LC record available at https://lccn.loc.gov/2021001539
LC ebook record available at https://lccn.loc.gov/2021001540

ISBN: 978-0-367-49458-2 (hbk)
ISBN: 978-0-367-49457-5 (pbk)
ISBN: 978-1-003-04904-3 (ebk)

Typeset in Times New Roman
by MPS Limited, Dehradun

This book is dedicated to my son, Jackson. To the pure light that you were. To the man you would have become. I walk in your light.

Contents

About the Author

Brian Miller, PhD, provides training and consultation on topics of secondary trauma, trauma-informed supervision, and implementation processes nationally and internationally. He is an individual member of the National Child Traumatic Stress Network (NCTSN) and chaired the NCTSN Secondary Trauma Supervision Workgroup. He is the developer of the CE-CERT model for intervening with secondary trauma in service providers and the Shielding model of trauma-informed supervision, both of which have been published and disseminated across mental health and child welfare systems.

Dr. Miller's experience includes tenure as director of Children's Behavioral Health at Primary Children's Hospital, director of Mental Health Services for Salt Lake County; director of the Trauma Program for Families with Young Children at The Children's Center in Salt Lake City; clinical director of Davis Behavioral Health, associate director of the Utah State Division of Mental Health; and as a psychotherapist in private practice. He holds a PhD from Case Western Reserve in Cleveland, Ohio, where he was a Mandel Leadership Fellow. He is the past board president for the National Alliance on Mental Illness, Utah Chapter, and serves on the editorial review boards for the journals *Traumatology* and *Contemporary Psychotherapy.*

Acknowledgments

All of the research that I cite in this book serves only to support what I learned first from the masters who practice their healing arts with native ability. Thank you to the passionately committed psychotherapists that I have been honored to work alongside and to formally interview. You practice all of these skills, without even realizing what you have taught me.

I wish to thank Irish, the pediatric oncology nurse who cared for my son and who naturally embodied all of these skills. I know that you wouldn't use this language, but I hope I gave vocabulary to what you do. I watched you as you felt the enormity of children's pain and the suffering of parents, yet allowed it to be felt through on a daily basis.

Thank you to the very accomplished Dr. Ginny Sprang who, upon hearing the raw concepts that became this book, leaned over to me at precisely the right time and said, "You should write a paper about this". You possess the rare combination of deep academic knowledge and the art of making things happen. You think deeply, and you do much.

Thank you to Françoise Mathieu, author of *The Compassion Fatigue Workbook* and presenter extraordinaire. Where one would expect protectiveness, I found only generosity. Thank you for opening this door to me. I am grateful for your giving heart.

To my partner, Lori, for being first reader and my first responder. In a year of pandemics, earthquakes, hurricanes, two moves, two deaths, and a snappish partner you came through with grace and kindness.

Thank you, Nicholas, for the Nigerian Jazz that served as background to my writing.

Foreword

I began my career as a mental health provider over 25 years ago, equipped with little more than a big heart and minimal training. From the outset, and probably due to a combination of personal disposition and my own family history, I was particularly drawn to crisis work. I volunteered in a hospital emergency ward and worked with soldiers returning from combat and with young adults experiencing life-altering tragedies.

The work was deeply engaging, yet the stories often disturbing. I struggled regularly with "impostor syndrome"; although, in this instance, it wasn't due to skewed low confidence in my clinical skills—it was caused by the realization that I was indeed woefully under-trained and often lacked the tools and resources to effectively help individuals who were in the midst of some the most difficult moments of their lives.

In the early days of this journey as a trauma worker, I started noticing that some of my colleagues were openly expressing cynicism and negativity towards their workplace and, at times, sadly, towards their patients. Conversely, other helping professionals seemed incredibly *well,* and many of those compassionate and engaged clinicians were providers with decades of experience. Many years of exposure did not appear to have damaged their empathic engagement.

For a novice, this raised a multitude of questions: why did clinical work with some patients feel depleting, yet other similarly challenging cases leave me energized? Why was it at times difficult to enjoy socializing with "civilians" who did not work in this field? Why were some service providers healthy and compassionate after years of service and others burned out after five years? What helped? Did self-care help? What about reducing caseloads? Which elements were within the purview of organizations and systems rather than the responsibility of individual workers? Why did I love this work so much and yet feel exhausted and depersonalized at times? Was there a roadmap for navigating trauma work and providing good quality ethical care? What about addressing poverty and barriers to resources? What were the hidden costs of ignoring these questions for us as a civil society? There were far more questions than there seemed to be answers.

These queries shaped and accidentally formed my second career as a secondary traumatic stress (STS) educator, and looking for empirical data and actionable solutions to STS has led me on one of the most interesting and rewarding journeys that a professional could possibly ask for. In 2015, a group of trauma specialists decided to create a think tank on provider impairment. We committed to meeting regularly to explore evidence-based research on STS with the hope of offering consensus-based best practice guidelines to helping professionals. This gathering of "STS geeks" is how I had the incredibly good fortune of meeting Brian Miller.

But I am getting ahead of myself—let's briefly go back in time, so that I can better anchor what an important contribution Brian's book is to the field of STS.

Research on provider impairment began in the 1970s with the work of psychologists Herbert Freudenberger and Christina Maslach as they explored a syndrome that they called "burnout". These researchers were seeking to describe the emotional and physical exhaustion that service providers developed as a result of the nature and experience of their working conditions. However, it was not until the 1990s that trauma experts such as Laurie Anne Pearlman, Charles Figley, and their colleagues began positing that provider impairment was far more complex and multifactorial than had originally been suggested. They felt that the term "burnout" was not a broad enough concept to capture and address the phenomena. Pearlman, Figley, and others argued that there was a need to explore the impact of *indirect* exposure to trauma and how personal, professional, and organizational factors contributed to a helping professional's resiliency and/or impairment.

First, and this was no small feat, they needed to convince decision-makers that indirect trauma indeed existed as a clinical manifestation and was deserving of attention. Over time, they succeeded in making their case. Unfortunately, as is often the way with societal shifts, many enthusiastic workplaces showed mission drift from the original thinkers' intent: the 2000s saw organizations suggesting that individual self-care practices and work–life balance were the key strategies to reduce provider impairment. This was scientifically unverified as there was very little evidence that these practices were effective without being embedded in a larger framework of provider well-being. It also distracted from much attention being given to the complexity of the systems and organizations within which STS occurred. Although many Human Resource departments were now paying lip-service to "workplace wellness", few providers were being offered tools to reset their nervous systems before, during, and after challenging cases, nor were they being given a forum to process morally distressing events. And, of course, the volume of work and reduction of referral resources continued unabated.

As I have written elsewhere, a quarter of a century after the emergence of the field of STS, it gradually became clear that collapsing on a yoga mat at the end of a challenging and exhausting week was not quite the magic bullet that many had hoped for. Over time, service providers began to express their frustration with mandatory workplace "self-care" trainings.

During this time, other experts in the field began suggesting that in order to be able to do trauma work, we needed to put on a virtual "haz-mat suit" and protect ourselves from caustic content. The belief (still widely popular today) was that the best way to keep secondary trauma and work-related burnout at bay was through avoidance and a certain amount of deliberate dissociation. I was once told by a child abuse investigator that I was "taking away his armor" by suggesting that he use empathic engagement and a trauma-informed approach in his work with traumatized children. But I have seen too many trauma-exposed professionals "cowboy up" (to borrow Brian's expression) during the course of their workday only to turn to self-medication, social isolation, hours of Internet watching, and other forms of numbing for me to accept that this is an effective strategy. Nor do I believe that it leads to good clinical outcomes for our patients. As you will see in this book, Brian posits that the notion of a "haz-mat" suit against indirect trauma is patently incorrect. Instead, equipped with solid empirical evidence, he argues—and this may seem counter-intuitive to some readers—that what we need to do instead is to "have [our] heart broken by [our] patients day after day" and that avoiding our internal experiences is far more perilous to our psychological well-being than being fully present to suffering.

In 2007, Brian published a study where he explored career-sustaining behaviors in those he called "passionately committed psychotherapists". His research demonstrated that these practitioners had identified that some of the protective factors for them involved maintaining a deep connection to a sense of vocation and an openness to having an ongoing internal dialogue about their work. Brian calls this process "the conscious narrative" and demonstrates that the key is to remain open to even the most challenging or tedious parts of our work, while continuously remaining aware and connected to our feelings, both positive and negative.

Over time, exploring the science of provider engagement inspired Brian to develop the CE-CERT model that is the backbone of this book. CE-CERT is a "synthetic" framework, which means that it integrates empirical findings from a wide variety of fields. The model provides concrete strategies to manage rumination and reduce emotional labor and argues that we need to learn to process and metabolize exposure before, during, and after the work is done. Finally, it emphasizes that like these "passionately committed thera-pists" we need to frame the stories (our own and our clients) in an "intentional narrative" in order to remain healthy and connected to the work.

Before you keep reading, I want to offer you a gentle word of warning: Brian is a disruptive thinker, and he challenges many of our accepted and homespun truths. What he suggests is provocative and may feel jarring at first. What you will find in the following pages proposes a reframing of the work as not inherently harmful to us. We do not need, Brian convincingly demonstrates, to protect ourselves from trauma stories; we need tools to remain connected to ourselves and to our breath.

If you have ever had the pleasure of hearing Brian present, you will know that he is a gifted wordsmith with a unique talent for sharing evocative metaphors and parables. This is a book that deserves to be read slowly, with notepad in hand and time for pause and reflection. Part of the challenge and beauty of this work is that it debunks some of our most cherished beliefs about helper wellness. If one of the components startles you or makes you feel defensive, as it did for me upon first reading, that is a good sign, in my opinion, as this is where the real work begins.

It seems fitting to have begun writing this foreword on the evening of Winter Solstice 2020—the longest night of the year in the Northern Hemisphere. For many of us, 2020 indeed felt like "the longest night of the year" as a global pandemic and profound social unrest shook our lives with what felt like no daybreak in sight. For essential workers, it has also been a time of increased workloads and pressures. The urgent need for strategies to address STS existed far before this current moment in history, but the stressors have become amplified for many of us. I believe that we need Brian's wisdom more than ever, and I cannot think of a better time for this book.

So, if you will, dear reader, please join me now on the powerful journey of the coming pages. If you are currently on the fence about your calling, this book may even bring you back to loving the work that you do.

Françoise Mathieu
December 21, 2020

Section I

Where We Begin: The Ordinary and Familiar World

1   Accepting the Challenge

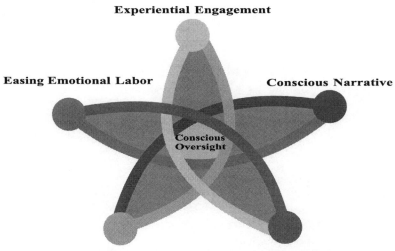

Experiential Engagement

Easing Emotional Labor

Conscious Narrative

Conscious Oversight

Reducing Rumination   **Parasympathetic Recovery**

It is easy to work when the soul is at play.

Emily Dickenson

Introduction

Consider those who really do feel like their "soul is at play" when they are at work. Now contrast them with Drew Carey's description: "Oh, you hate your job? Why didn't you say so? There's a support group for that. It's called everybody, and they meet at the bar". (Carey, Helford, Graham & Cohen, 1998) Which better describes you? What is it that makes the difference—something we are doing, or is it something about our job? Surely, there are unique aspects when your job is treating people who have experienced trauma.

Secondary trauma. Compassion fatigue. Moral distress. Burnout. Good old-fashioned stress. Different concepts—yet inter-related phenomenon. All of these hazards have one thing in common: they describe the emotional toll of the work of the helping professions. And the emotion work of treating trauma takes its own unique toll.

This effect goes beyond "the cost of caring". In fact, sometimes the demands of the job allow little space for caring: the intensity of the reactions in our clients, constant immersion in trauma imagery, insufficient resources, and lack of freedom to do our jobs the way we would like to. We might even be willing to trade the *real* source of job pressure for the problem of "caring too much". Far from being drained by too much caring, we hunger for more time in that place of compassion that drew us into the field. The problem isn't too much caring. It is that there is so much pressure, and so many distractions, that we get there only too rarely.

The Seed Crystal for This Book

I was listening to a podcast in which an author said something like, "If you see a book on managing anxiety, you can bet that the author has difficulty managing anxiety". I immediately saw the truth in that. And if you see a book on managing the effects of secondary trauma, you can bet that the author—me—has had difficulty managing the effects of this emotion work.

Early in my clinical career, I divided my work time between private psychotherapy patients and group treatment in a partial hospitalization program that I had developed with two colleagues. As it happened, the partial hospital program drew patients who were chronically suicidal, had extensive trauma histories, were "treatment resistant", and often engaged in parasuicidal behaviors. Unintentionally, my referral network for my individual practice was the same as the partial hospital program. That meant that in my private practice I was also seeing almost exclusively these very complex and difficult clients. I remember long days of facilitating groups with patients who were in suicidal crisis, re-experiencing trauma, and leaving group to self-injure, followed by individual sessions with my private patients who were also often in suicidal crisis, re-experiencing trauma, and dealing with self-injurious behaviors such as cutting and burning.

I have a "flashbulb" memory of one of those days when I was facilitating a group while one group member was screaming in terror at the revivification of her childhood trauma, which triggered another group member who was curled around a pillow in a prenatal position, totally unresponsive to any supports I offered. I feared not only for my patients, but also that the lawyers in the office next door would advocate for our eviction. Meanwhile, a third group member had left the group to go into the restroom to begin self-cutting. After coaxing her back into the group, the remainder of the group time was spent negotiating with the group members, several of whom said they could not go home because they were triggered and suicidal. After conducting a risk assessment of each group member and ending the group, I spent several hours providing support to the two most activated group members. My evening was spent on the phone providing in-home coaching of emotion regulation skills to various group members late into the night. Then, to wake up and begin to do it all again...

If you are asking yourself about the effectiveness of treatment with this clinical mix in this setting, you are asking a reasonable question (but one beyond the scope of this book). Rather, my focus is on the emotional toll that this work was taking on me. I heard someone describe a day that matched my level of stress as "one of those days when your brain turns to putty, begins to leak out of your nose and your inner ear begins to bleed…" It wasn't that I "cared too much". I was in survival mode, worried about these women, worried about my own risk management/ liability issues dealing with so much suicidality, grasping for the appropriate clinical interventions, worried about getting evicted. Compassion resides in the anterior cingulate cortex. Compassion is only accessible to us when we are calm and safe, not when we are in fight or flight—as I was. This wasn't compassion fatigue, because I hadn't touched compassion once that day.

I eventually left this situation to escape the secondary trauma that I was experiencing (and the burnout, job stress, moral distress—I had them all). When I returned to clinical practice, I passionately pursued answers about how to flourish in this work. I spent as much energy figuring that out as I did acquiring new clinical skills. I came to believe that the skills that would allow me to emotionally flourish were foundational to client relationship skills and clinical interventions. I continue to believe our clinical interventions will fail unless we possess equal skillfulness in our own emotion regulation.

I began making adjustments that enhanced the rewards of doing psychotherapy. I conducted years of informal observation of psychotherapists who were "on fire" and those who were "burned out". I noted the irony that the ones who burned out had never been on fire, and the ones who were on fire seemed to never burn out. I realized that the conceptual inaccuracies implicit in terms like "burnout" and "compassion fatigue" took us in wrong directions. I did formal research on "passionately committed" psychotherapists to understand the strategies that they employed to sustain over long careers. I immersed myself in the trauma treatment literature and other bodies of research literature outside of what I call the "burnout echo chamber". This included literature as varied as occupational psychology, neurophysiology, cognitive behavioral therapy, and cognitive narratology.

This is a book about secondary traumatic stress (STS), and I will maintain a focus on strategies for managing STS. But you will also note that I often use the string of STS, compassion fatigue, burnout, job stress. Because—although there certainly are conceptual and definitional distinctions between STS and those concepts—the common factors between them and the way these phenomena inter-gear makes clear that the same emotion regulation strategies can mediate those stressors as well.

I will describe concrete, evidence-informed strategies that can sustain a career for persons doing trauma work. And they aren't the strategies proposed in the popular wisdom about "burnout" or "compassion fatigue". This isn't a book about self-care, nor is it about how to find "work–life balance". In fact, those notions may be taking us in precisely the wrong direction and away from the evidence.

The strategies I have synthesized here derive from what we know about trauma. What we know about emotion regulation. What we know about emotional labor. What we know about autonomic arousal and parasympathetic recovery. What we know about the emotion centers of the brain and how those centers link and communicate with the autonomic nervous system and the "higher brain", the story and meaning-making part of the cerebral cortex. We know a lot—but we have allowed solutions to our job distress to develop from the popular media/social networks rather than from sound wisdom grounded in empiricism. The wisdom that I synthesize has been scattered in different fields, and in different bodies of literature. I have gathered it here.

CE-CERT (Components for Enhancing Clinician Experience and Reducing Trauma)

I have synthesized empirically informed strategies into a model I call CE-CERT (Components for Enhancing Clinician Experience and Reducing Trauma). Let me explain the CE-CERT acronym: 1) "Clinician" notes the primary target when the model was developed—reducing STS in trauma clinicians. However, because the skills are directed at the management of emotion dysregulation, the model is just as applicable to those of you who are not in clinical roles. Trauma clinicians aren't the only ones who experience the effects of secondary trauma. 2) "Components" communicates that the model identifies strategies derived from disparate research literature fields. CE-CERT synthesizes these concepts into one, unified model. 3) "Enhancing experience" specifies something important: the function of CE-CERT is not only to reduce STS but also to sustain your career as a trauma worker. When your experience of doing the work in the moment is improved, that, in turn, facilitates the reduction of secondary trauma. 4) Lastly, the "reducing trauma" aspect of CE-CERT directly targets the causes, symptoms, and sequalae of indirect exposure to trauma. As I will demonstrate, STS can be mediated—and even prevented—once we understand its causes and acquire skills that prepare us for it.

The Structure of this Book

The Three Act Story Structure

This book is structured in the three acts of the classical story. This three-act structure is important to the concept of cognitive breathing and replicates the way that our brains deal with stress events. In Chapter 4, I will discuss the conscious narrative, and the way in which our brain cries out for a beginning, middle, and end to any intense experience. These are the three acts to a classical adventure tale, and they are also the three acts of our story: 1) *Beginning:* living in the ordinary world and the call to leave the familiar; 2) *Middle:* the "challenge", entering the new world; and 3) *End:* returning home with new wisdom. Recovery from stress and trauma exposure requires that we fully experience all three acts. This book—and indeed all stories—parallel the breath in this way: *Act I:* the beginning (focusing attention on the breath); *Act II:* the challenge (the inbreath) and *Act III:* the return (the exhale).

Cognitive Breathing

"Just breathe". Perhaps, when you are dealing with intense stress, someone telling you to "just breathe" is exactly what you need to hear. Or, if you are more like me, it feels like trivial advice. But it is worth thinking about breathing for a moment. Why is the focus on the breath the bedrock of stress reduction and mindfulness? Breathing is the tai chi—yin and yang—animated: inhale and exhale, contract and relax, lean in and lean out, sympathetic response and parasympathetic response.

This is a book about breathing. In fact, the first working title for this book was "Cognitive Breathing". But one of the earliest reviewers said that term make her think of the baseball pitcher in the movie *Bull Durham,* who would focus his pitches by trying to breathe through his eyelids. And that's certainly not the image I wish to evoke here. Nor am I referring to the literal, through-the-nose-into-the-lungs breathing, although that kind of breathing is functionally related. And—if you are feeling stressed or feeling run down on your job—you might need some help with that kind of breathing as well.

Cognitive breathing changes the way we think about STS and job stress. It is learning to "breathe" in the sense of allowing the natural rises and falls of thought/emotion/stress/recovery. How do we open the pathways for a full mental, emotional and experiential inhalation, and then how do we fully exhale to complete the natural process? The novelist Anne Tyler entitled one of her books *Breathing Lessons*, and in the figurative sense, that title that could work here as well.

As the concepts of this book unfold, you will see that the skills and practices of cognitive breathing are all in service of keeping our natural, metabolic processes moving without interruption. These cognitive and physiological processes are dynamic, energy-driven systems. Peter Levine said that trauma is "the result of a normal process that is not allowed to come to completion" (Levine & Frederick, 1997). In the same way, secondary trauma—a form of trauma—is the result of interrupting the natural waves of stress throughout the day, freezing the process in the middle of the wave and not allowing its natural completion. We hold our breath to get through the day, rather than ever fully inhaling or fully exhaling. Inhaling in this context is the willingness to open to stressors and "breathe the experience in fully"; an inbreath should be equal to the exhalation, "breathing the experience out fully".

In a very material way, emotions and thoughts are metabolized by the body. Our brain possesses the ability to know and notice this natural course of beginning and end, but it also has the ability to avoid or even change this sense of flow. The brain can recreate the thoughts and feelings so that the metabolic process is endlessly recycled, and these feelings don't feel like a dynamic and time-limited process at all. We get stuck in the liminal space between ebb and flow and lose the sense of the motion of events. This is the stuff of chronic stress and chronic job distress. We don't feel like we just experienced a stressful or traumatic experience that is now over, but rather, we have the sense that we are swimming in an ocean of stress.

As we will see, when stressors are approached with intention and willingness—and when they are allowed to come to a finish—the character of the stress changes profoundly. The cognitive breath facilitates the rhythm and connectedness of the inhalation and the exhalation. It is seeing the wave and not just the ocean. It is trusting that if we learn how to stay out of the way, the wave always comes to the shore.

The potential of this entire enterprise—regulating our emotions in the face of secondary trauma—is tremendous. Ultimately, we are aiming to improve our ability to *consciously regulate autonomic dysregulation.* And if we can do that, it will change not only how we deal with stressors on the job, but also how we experience stress in our lives generally. The Buddhist priest Dogen said that "To study the Buddha Way is to study the self" (Strand, 2011). Likewise, the skills described in CE-CERT apply not only when we are exposed to trauma, but to all aspects of our lives.

Many of us in the helping professions need this kind of help. Trauma work and the helping professions—medicine, psychotherapy, child welfare, social services—are hard jobs. In a later chapter, we will examine exactly what makes emotion work difficult. But we can agree that they are stressful occupations. Everyone also agrees that these professions—roles that exist to help other people toward well-being—are noble professions. We must do something about the sad fact that we have known for at least 45 years since Freudenberger first proposed the notion of burnout: that many professionals doing this helping work are not flourishing.

The Ordinary World: Our Starting Place— "Treatment-As-Usual"

This chapter is the first act of our story. As with any story, it begins with setting the stage by describing the circumstances of the familiar world. This story starts where you are right now, and where you will be tomorrow if nothing changes—same trauma exposure, same stressors, and same reactions, same coping strategies. Let's describe our surroundings at the beginning of our journey. At present, this is what the terrain looks like for helping professionals:

Rates of Burnout, Compassion Fatigue, Secondary Trauma Are High

This book addresses STS. The skills defined here will improve your ability to manage stress and the emotion dysregulation that occurs due to trauma exposure. Secondary trauma inter-gears with—and has a two-way relationship with—related concepts such as burnout and compassion fatigue, and recent concepts such as moral distress. You have almost certainly seen some of the research describing the state of the field related to these phenomena, and it is troubling.

Establishing the precise prevalence of any of these conditions by profession is impossible. Researchers have employed these different but overlapping concepts, selected samples in a variety of ways (rarely randomized), sometimes used clinical cutoff scores, or sometimes sorted scores nominally. In short, their methods and definitions have varied so much that we don't have any kind of gold standard. Furthermore, for most professional groups, prevalence of STS has been too rarely studied in large-enough samples for us to draw conclusions. But to help us understand the professional world in which we are living, here are some research findings related to the more established concept of burnout. We know that there is a very high correlation between rates of STS and burnout (Cieslak et al., 2014).

Widely different figures have been cited for percentages of physicians who meet criteria for burnout—from as low as 0% to as high as 80.5%. A range that large says a lot about the lack of research definitions and not so much about actual physician burnout. An often-cited figure is that one half of all physicians show standardized burnout scores above the significance cutoff. Some studies show different rates based on specialty, for example, urology (63.6%); physical medicine and rehabilitation (63.3%); family medicine (63.0%); radiology (61.4%); orthopedic surgery (59.6%); dermatology (56.5%); general surgery subspecialties (52.7%); pathology (52.5%); and general pediatrics (46.3%). And across most studies, this problem of physicians who experience burnout is not getting better—it is becoming markedly worse.

In nurses, burnout rates are similarly varied depending upon the methodology and area of nursing practice. A review of the literature provided, again, a dizzying range in burnout rates from 0% to 70% (Van Mol et al., 2015). A 2018 meta-analysis, however, cited a burnout rate of over half, 52% in nurses across specialties (Zhang et al., 2018).

Mental health professionals have followed burnout rates amongst their own ranks since the 1980s. A recent meta-analysis of high-quality studies yielded that approximately 40% of mental health professionals manifest high levels of burnout in at least one domain (O'Connor et al., 2018).

Among child welfare workers, studies show the incidence of burnout and compassion fatigue also often hits near the 50% mark. As with studies of other professions, the data are very flawed and are often limited to a particular state or even county. Nonetheless, studies of child welfare workers in state systems return prevalence numbers of burnout and compassion fatigue between 44% and 50% (Conrad & Kellar-Guenther, 2006; Rothenberg et al., 2008). It is worth noting, however, that several studies have shown that those working in Child Welfare have increased risk of both burnout and STS as compared to other helping professions (Kim, 2011; Sprang et al., 2011).

Regardless of professional guild, or where you practice, a higher rate of trauma cases increases your risk of having symptoms of STS (Craig & Sprang, 2010). It makes sense on its face that the more trauma you are exposed to, the more secondary trauma you will experience. But I will have a great deal to say about mitigating this correlation later in this book—and those of you who are caring for a large number of clients with trauma will be heartened by your ability to reduce the strength of this correlation.

The state of the prevalence research on burnout, compassion fatigue, and secondary trauma is a mess. But there is a convergence—at least in meta-analyses—that approximately 50% of helping professionals are experiencing some form of significant distress that results from their work.

I once heard an anecdote describing how fuzzy logic can actually lead to more precision in some circumstances:

Father:	"Boys, what is the distance between the moon and the earth?"
Youngest Son:	"Very far away".
Oldest Son:	"It is 225,000 miles away".

In fact, the younger son's answer, "very far away", is at times the most precise answer. Depending on the position of the moon's approach, the oldest son could be off by as many as 27,000 miles. But the youngest son is always correct.

Employing that logic, let's settle on that rather fuzzy figure that about half of helping professionals are struggling with some form of job distress. It's not a bold statement to say that a rate of professional distress of 50% is simply too high. These professionals—including you—contribute an invaluable service to the individuals for whom they care. These professionals—including you—improve the communities where they live. We don't know how many of these highly educated professionals choose to leave their professional roles, and their accumulated knowledge and expertise is lost. Or how many stay, but suffer through their workdays with little satisfaction and significant stress. Or how many exhibit "presenteeism", in which they are on the job in body only but have lost the passion for their work.

We begin our journey where *you* are right now. Reflect on the question for yourself at this time. Prevalence data can help assure you that you are not alone, but your individualized answer is what matters here. Are you experiencing distress or disaffection from your job due to secondary trauma, burnout, or compassion fatigue? Is it better, worse, or the same as last year at this time? Is it better, worse, or the same as when you first came to this work?

Look again at the dates of the citations on burnout rates among helping professionals. These prevalence numbers are relatively recent—yet, we have been talking about burnout for nearly a half-century. We don't have data points trustworthy enough to conclude confidently what is happening to the professional burnout rates over that time, but we have enough data to know one thing with perfect clarity: rates of professional distress in the helping professions remain unacceptably high. So here is where we begin our journey: you are at risk. We need you to stay well to do this important work. And what we have been doing isn't working.

The Ordinary World—What We Are Doing Isn't Working

As we prepare to venture beyond this known world, we should first consider what went wrong here. What is the common factor across the "treatment-as-usual" strategies? The answer—whether we are examining self-care, work–life balance, or even mindful meditation—is that these approaches take aim at supporting *after-work recovery*. At worst, this is a hold-on-until-you-can-get-home strategy. At best, this recovery-after-work approach confers some hardiness that will carry into your workdays. There is evidence that this could be true for some stress conditions, especially when mindfulness meditation is consistently applied (Luken & Sammons, 2016).

Self-care would be the solution to secondary trauma/burnout if these conditions resulted from insufficient self-care in the first place. But secondary trauma is, of course, more complex than that. To adequately explain the emotional strain on trauma workers, one would have to imagine a complex Venn diagram with scores of overlapping and interacting spheres. Factors that would necessarily be included would be the volume of job demand (e.g., caseloads or productivity requirements); the temperament of the professional (e.g., trait anxiety); the level of social support experienced by the professional; the organizational climate of the employing agency (e.g., the perceived level of support from executive officers); goodness-of-fit between the professional and the job role; level of conflict/hostility in colleagues; and degree and amount of trauma exposure. More than four decades of burnout research have identified scores of other correlates—if not causes—of burnout. When you consider the number of complex factors, and the inter-gearing of those factors that contribute to secondary trauma, compassion fatigue, and burnout, it becomes obvious why the simple solutions that we have been touting have failed to help.

Recover-after-work approaches are based on a faulty metaphor that I call the bucket theory. Bucket theory invokes two buckets. One of those buckets holds all of the accumulated stress of your workdays. Each day, you add more stress to that bucket. When the bucket gets full, you are overcome with a need to get away, to go somewhere restorative so you can empty that bucket (and create space for future stress). The whole notion of work–life balance is very much predicated on the metaphor of the stress bucket, and the need to empty that bucket before it is too late. Built into this metaphor is that *the stress bucket is filled at work and is emptied at leisure.*

The second bucket contains your compassion for people for whom you care. With the compassion bucket, the goal is to be careful not to empty your bucket too soon. Each time you experience compassion, you take something out of that bucket. If you work in an intense environment, you may become desensitized to the suffering of your patients. You may have dulled your emotional experience as a defense mechanism, or it may have been a by-product of years of exposure. The notion of compassion fatigue is very much predicated on the metaphor of the compassion bucket. If we experience too much compassion—give too much away—our bucket will become empty before our career ends. The goal, I suppose, is to give out that last bit of empathy on our last day of work.

Here's the thing: neither of these buckets exist in reality. At least, neither of these buckets exist outside of the story that you are telling yourself. But in your story those buckets become reified. These narratives produce real negative effects when we believe them. Both stress and compassion are energy-driven emotional states. They are *energies*. The flaw of the bucket metaphors is that they suggest stress and compassion are static states that can be stored or imparted. But energy states will rise and fall and can be neither saved nor dispensed at will.

The implicit premise of these treatment-as-usual approaches is that if you de-stress enough, find enough pleasure or recreation, or find the family time that you have been missing due to your slavish devotion to work, your stress bucket will be lightened. And once your stress bucket is empty, it will be easier for you to re-enter the stress field of work because you have cleared all that space. It's an emotionally appealing story.

Perhaps it operates like that—maybe emptying our stress bucket leads to rest during the weekend so you can run on that energy all week—sometimes. Given that we have scarce research on the effectiveness of these recovery-after-work approaches, answer this honestly for yourself: have you found that practicing these empty-out-my-bucket strategies provides you with the sense of equilibrium and energy that carries you through your work week? How long has it been since you had the feeling that your stress bucket was empty, and your compassion bucket was full? Or is one of the sources of your stress the fact that it has been too long since you felt totally renewed, and that you never seem to have time to get to those things that would restore you?

Research has shown that vacations from work are good for our mental and physical health, but also that the effects of a vacation on our work stress are very short-lived (Etzion, 2003). A vacation could be so thoroughly enjoyable that we completely de-stress and by the time it is over we are chomping at the bit to get back to work. Or, the vacation could be so thoroughly enjoyable, and the feeling of being stress-free so nice, that the first Monday back on the job is even more onerous to anticipate. In the work–life balance paradigm, maybe it is dangerous to ungird our loins.

Recovering after a stressful workday is a fine idea. I know that, and you know that. Finding time for pleasurable and valued activities—prioritizing how we spend our limited resource of time—is also a fine idea. I am not suggesting these things don't matter. Rather, I am saying that emphasis on recovering after work will not resolve—and has not resolved—these complex conditions. Not secondary trauma. Not compassion fatigue. Not burnout.

The Call to Adventure: Leaving the Ordinary World

The Three Blasphemies

Treatment-as-usual for burnout, compassion fatigue, and STS is based on received wisdom. We have passed along the popular wisdom of self-care and work–life balance, but we haven't empirically observed whether that advice was working. I aim to disabuse our field of some of our sacred mountains. I term these challenges "blasphemies", because they are in stark contrast to the received wisdom. Here is where we leave the familiar:

The First Blasphemy: Burnout Is a Myth

To be sure, as I have reported above, many in the helping professions return high scores on the Maslach Burnout Inventory, a standardized measurement with good psychometric properties. Why, then, am I proclaiming that burnout is a myth? Consider the term "burnout" in the literal sense: A thing is set afire, burns brightly, burns up its energy source, and then burns out. But this process of catching fire, burning more brightly, and then burning out, isn't the course of professional burnout at all.

Freudenberger coined the term "burnout" in 1974 to describe the chronic course of depletion in staff members. He suggested that burnout happened to those who are overcommitted and too idealistic. But subsequent research has revealed that the concept doesn't hold up. First, the natural history of burnout is not one of the professional having high energy and dedication early in their career and then steadily losing motivation and feeling more "burned out" over the course of their career.

Multiple studies have established that burnout is highest *early* in one's career and is steady thereafter—except on some measures when it is actually *negatively correlated* (it goes down) with time in the job (Fagin et al., 1996; Söderfeldt et al., 1995; Sullivan & Nashman, 1999) Mental health workers in particular show higher burnout scores early in their career than they do later, revealing the error in conceptualizing burnout as degrading one's professional motivation over time (Volpe et al., 2014). Even Maslach herself, developer of the Maslach Burnout Inventory, described that burnout was chronic and stable, not accumulating, over one's career (Maslach & Schaufeli, 1993).

I am encouraged that years of experience actually have a positive effect on emotional exhaustion and sense of personal accomplishment (Carney et al., 1993; Tamura et al., 1995; Van der Ploeg et al., 1990). We *should* feel a greater sense of fulfillment as our body of work grows—not a sense of depletion, but a growing sense of having contributed. And the evidence is, in fact, that this is the case for many of us. Burnout isn't inevitable, nor is it "just what happens" to those of us in the helping professions. Feelings of burnout should be urgently responded to and not passively accepted as the normal course of one's work. This is even true of roles with high levels of trauma exposure.

The second of Freudenberger's assertions—that the source of burnout is over-commitment to a cause—has also been debunked by the ensuing research. In fact, the best predictor of career burnout is *avoidance*, the exact opposite of over-commitment (Iglesias et al., 2010; Kroska et al., 2017; Naidoo et al., 2012; Polman et al., 2010). Because both burnout and STS correlate with experiential *avoidance*, enhancing experiential *engagement* is a foundational skill in the CE-CERT model.

The Second Blasphemy: Compassion Fatigue Is a Misnomer

Most of us entered the helping professions because we desired to be compassionate helpers for those who need us. This urge-toward-compassion is precisely why we do what we do. The misnomer of compassion fatigue misses an important, demonstrable fact: when we are sitting before a client and we are experiencing compassion for that person, it is a *pleasurable*, not an effortful sensation. Indeed, when compassion is experienced, there is activity in the nucleus accumbens, the reward center of the brain. Perhaps the height of the misnomer about compassion as fatiguing is a published journal article that argued that burnout served a protective function because it reduced our empathy. In this way, the author argues, burnout is a good thing because it protects us from compassion fatigue. If burnout is desirable because it protects us from compassion fatigue, both you and I are in the wrong profession.

Fortunately, compassion isn't fatiguing, and it never was. There is solid empirical evidence that compassion/empathy inoculates us against, rather than causes, secondary trauma and burnout (Klimecki & Singer, 2012;

Wagaman et al., 2015; Wilkinson et al., 2017). In fact, the more frequently we experience compassion, the better we are at our job and the more we will enjoy it. One study found that when empathy declines, the distress of the work doesn't diminish, but the positive aspects of the work decline (Fernando & Consedine, 2014). When looking at fMRI images of physicians' brains, low empathy predicted higher burnout. Intriguingly, these researchers speculated that perhaps a physician's inability to experience and identify their emotions was the causative factor. As you will see, this finding is utterly consistent with the CE-CERT model and the skills that will correct for this inability.

What has, unfortunately, been termed "compassion fatigue" is actually compassion *strain*—straining to get to compassion—not experiencing too much of it, but rather, too little of it. When job factors don't allow us to experience compassion—documentation demands, conflict on treatment teams, uncooperative clients, unwieldy caseloads—that is draining. But we aren't depleted because we expended all of the compassion from our "compassion bucket". As I will present in Chapter 7, experiencing compassion *more often* actually reduces the emotional labor of our jobs—and enhances our job satisfaction.

The Third Blasphemy: Secondary Trauma Isn't Caused by Exposure to Too Much Intensity

Neither primary nor secondary trauma is caused by exposure to intensity—not intense situations, not intense emotion. Rather—and this is important—trauma is produced by *feelings of helplessness or feelings of being overwhelmed* in the face of a threat to our well-being. Remember these two conditions: 1) helplessness and 2) overwhelm, as they are fundamental to mitigating the effects of secondary trauma. Secondary trauma occurs when you freeze before intensity—interrupting the stress cycle. This freezing happens when you become *overwhelmed* by exposure events or you feel *helpless* before them.

The CE-CERT skills actively target these sensations of helplessness and overwhelm. Protecting yourself from secondary trauma is a skill that is acquired, just as is any clinical skill. Unfortunately, however, our educational programs prepared us to provide clinical interventions, but failed to offer these foundational skills.

Accepting the Challenge: Moving from Traditional Wisdom to What Works

Changing Our Experience in Real Time

The change in perspective away from work–life balance and self-care is crucial to understanding the CE-CERT model. We are focusing on becoming more skillful at cognitive breathing. This perspective change shifts us toward dealing with job distress *in situ*—in place, on-the-job, and in real time. Not recovery after work, but keeping the energies moving as part of a natural metabolic process *during* work. Becoming skillful in these practices is a developmental skills approach of the highest order. How do we metabolize work stress as it occurs? How do we learn to willingly "inhale" the stress, and learn to "exhale" to clear that event? How do we prevent STS? What does metabolizing stress look like in the real, clinical setting?

The goal of cognitive breathing is to improve the experience of your work *while you work*—the aversive job tasks, as well as the enjoyable job tasks. Elizabeth Barrett Browning wrote, "I love you not only for what you are, but for what I am when I am with you. I love you not only for what you have made of yourself, but for what you are making of me. I love you for the part of me that you bring out" (Caraballo, 2014). What Browning said in the poem can be distilled into a more prosaic truth: we like people—and situations—that create a positive feeling in us. We could move this simple truth into the context of our work: "I like my job not only for what it is, but for the part of me it brings out". Which implies its opposite: "I don't like my job because of the way I feel when I am doing my work". As obvious as this statement seems here, I am making an important dissection: we have two discrete variables at play. Not just "my work" but also "the way I feel when I do my work". I am targeting the way you feel when you do your work.

If you are working in an unhealthy or untenable job situation, I'm not suggesting you should change the way you feel about it. Maybe upon rational assessment you really aren't a good fit either for your current workplace or job role. We will return to this topic in Chapter 7, when I will discuss the importance of conserving your energy by answering the question about your goodness-of-fit in a decisive way. But for now, let's stipulate that you aren't going to change your work. So, we will focus on changing how you feel when you do your work.

A recent meme proposes a message exchange between an employer and an employee:

Every Company: "We'd like to promote mental well-being in the workplace".

Every Employee: "How about hiring more people so we won't feel so pressured, and raising our pay so we can keep up with the spiraling cost of living and aren't stressing about paying our bills".

Every Company: "No, not that. Try Yoga".

Your list may be a little different: "How about reducing the number of trauma clients on my caseload?"; "How about getting a better electronic medical record that doesn't double the time it takes for me to document my assessment and treatment?"; "How about reducing our caseloads by 25% so we have time to deliver good care?"; "How about adjusting productivity requirements to allow for lunch and bathroom breaks?"; or even "How about building a culture of teamwork and dealing with some of the toxic members of the team?"

And perhaps, as in the meme, your organization's response would be some version of "No, but we are starting a meditation group every second Thursday during lunch". When the cause of job distress is systemic, the solution cannot be individual employees doing some version of relaxation or self-care. Organizational factors are systemic and must be dealt with at a systems level.

CE-CERT defines a set of discrete skills. As imposing as it may seem to set a goal of "transforming the emotional experience of doing your work", it isn't as unattainable as it may sound. Detailed in this book is a set of practices to support emotion regulation. We have known these skills, and they have an evidence basis. You could say that they were hiding in plain sight. That is, they have been very evident in the professional research literature, but not in the "burnout" or "secondary trauma" literature. Rather, the CE-CERT skills are derived from other areas of study: the trauma-treatment research, neuroscience, narrative theory, cognitive behavioral therapy, and occupational psychology. Cognitive breathing uses the evidence supporting each of these practices and synthesizes them into a novel, skills-based approach to mediate the effects of STS and, more broadly, other sources of job distress.

Establishing Scaffolding for the Skills

As part of the call to leave the familiar world, consider if there are changes in your patterns that are needed in order to establish the scaffolding for the model I am introducing. The CE-CERT skills are supported by three behavioral shifts that may depart from what you are doing at present:

Conscious Reflection

The first element of the scaffolding for the CE-CERT skills is the practice of conscious reflection. This refers to paying continuous attention to key elements of your well-being, as well as to key signals of distress. You are your own well-being oversight committee. This means you will begin cultivating attention to how you are doing and what you are feeling in real time. By the time you finish this book, you will know where this attention should go.

This practice of scrupulously paying attention to your emotional and physical responses is probably different than what you are currently doing—it may even fly in the face of how you have been coping with job stressors. Many of us contend with stress by busying up so completely that we don't notice how we are feeling until we are at maximum stress. We may feel that we don't have the *time* to stop and take stock. Or we may avoid pausing for self-protective reasons. Deep down, we fear that we would be overwhelmed by it all if we paid attention—we fear all of our defenses would come crashing down.

Thomas Banacek, a character from a television show in the 1970s, offered this ostensibly Polish aphorism: "When your sleigh is being chased by wolves, throw them a sugar cookie, but don't stop to bake a cake". For some of us, the feeling of pressure may be so intense that paying attention feels like stopping to bake that cake. We don't dare attend to our emotions out of the belief that if we stop, the wolves will pounce. In Chapter 2, I will demonstrate how the sugar cookies that you have been throwing *have* distracted the wolves—but have also *fed* them. The more sugar cookies you throw, the more feelings of overwhelm grow, both in size and in menace.

Defining the Targets

Each of the developmental practices comprising CE-ERT begins with seeing the target at which we are aiming. This intentionality—setting out to do something with deliberateness—transforms even activities that you may be doing already, or trying to do already, into meaningful goals. Setting the target is the deliberate alignment of our aspiration, our thoughts and feelings, and our actions.

As I begin to describe each of the CE-CERT domains, the first action step is for you to see the target. When you are experiencing secondary trauma—or plain old job stress—what is it that you are currently trying to do in order to cope? What, exactly, is the target that you are trying to hit—other than "not get so stressed out"? The very basis of this book is an effort to define the problem of secondary trauma in a way it can be solved.

Florence Chadwick, the first woman to successfully swim the round-trip distance across the English Channel, failed in her first effort to swim the Catalina Channel on a foggy day. After swimming more than 16 hours, she quit a mere half-mile from her goal, the Palos Verde peninsula. She was beaten by the fog. "If I could have seen land, I might have made it", she said (Raga, 2017).

We are swimming in the fog when we experience STS, and we are distressed about it, but we feel that we are victims to the circumstances that produce it. We are swimming in the fog when we go in to work each day stressed but don't know what to attempt in order to fix it. Or we flail about attempting to find more time for "self-care" or better "work–life balance". We don't know where land is or how far away it is. Nobody can keep this high effort going forever when we don't know which way to swim or how long to keep stroking.

Making a meaningful change in your level of job distress or job satisfaction requires that you know what, exactly, you are aiming for. That is why, for each skill domain, I will begin by suggesting what the target looks like. See the land that you are navigating toward. Once you see it clearly, then, and only then, can you align your aspiration, your motivation, your thoughts, and your efforts. And—only when you have set your intention—will you know when those energies are misaligned, and the ways that you are dividing your efforts.

The relatively new area of research known as positive psychology—the science of what makes us happy—has yielded an interesting finding: 40% of a person's overall level of happiness owes to things that people do intentionally because they know it makes them happy (Sheldon & Lyubomirsky, 2006). In other words, people engage in these activities purely because they know those things make them happier. That is setting an intention. I believe that it is a fair extrapolation to expect that the same 40% of our job happiness owes to things we do to make our jobs more rewarding, more enjoyable. But, of course, we must know *what* those things are that increase our job happiness if we are going to engage them with intentionality. The CE-CERT model defines some of those strategies.

Substituting Active Responses for Passive Responses

All three elements supporting CE-CERT—conscious reflection, setting an intention, and substituting active responses for passive responses—are important. But nothing is more essential than substituting active responses for passivity. This element targets the very nature and origin of STS. Each of the CE-CERT skills are active skills that can be employed in circumstances in which you may have been passive heretofore.

I previously described that secondary trauma is produced when we reach the conclusion that "I am helpless to do anything about this" or "I am frozen by how overwhelming this is". Therefore, these sensations are key targets in addressing secondary trauma. I want you to know that when you are before a stressor, there is an action you can take. In the case of a primary trauma (e.g., a child who suffers abuse), conclusions of helplessness are based in fact. As children they were helpless to do anything to protect themselves from the trauma. But it is important in our strategy of protecting ourselves from secondary exposure that we do not parallel that conclusion. If we do, that is when the effects of STS accrue.

Unlike victims of primary trauma, the inference that we are helpless (passive) or overwhelmed can be challenged as untrue—which it usually is. And, when it is true—we really are overwhelmed—that fact is amenable to change. And that is exactly why it is important that we feel able to employ an *active* strategy as opposed to the feeling that we are being passively buffeted. Harm to our well-being or job satisfaction—exactly the effects of secondary trauma—occurs when we are in a stance of passiveness. Active responses result from feeling skilled and empowered.

Passive responses are often in the form of emotion-focused coping, trying to escape the stressor so we can emotionally restore ourselves. That is also why, when we are stressed, we have the strong desire to get away from work and get to the safe space of home. When we are at work, we have feelings of being overwhelmed, but when we are home, we feel more in control.

The late comedian Mitch Hedberg said, "I'm sick of following my dreams. I'm just gonna ask them where they're going and catch up with them later". Is this what you did with the aspirations you had for your job? Did you become passive in waiting for it to turn into the job that you wished it was? As I will discuss in Chapter 7, the first active response called for is for you to make an *active* (and reflective, informed) decision about whether you are in the right job in the right organization. It is important that this be a wholehearted decision instead of a daily or moment-by-moment internal debate. Once you have made this decision actively, energy is freed up for defining other active strategies for making the job feel better.

But within that disclaimer, I also have to admit that making those determinations (is it the job, is it the organization, or is it me?) is not easy. Indeed, we shouldn't trust the conclusions we make when we are emotionally dysregulated. In that way, CE-CERT skills may be helpful in leading you to an answer that isn't contaminated by your own emotional reaction. This caveat relates to advice I heard given to organizations: be aware that one of the unintended consequences of bringing mindfulness meditation into the workplace is that it won't make the employees more productive, but it may allow them to develop the clarity to realize that they need to leave.

I can hardly overstate the importance of an inner sense of awareness that you are in your job because you actively *decided* to be and because you believe you can make that role feel meaningful and—at least at times—deeply enjoyable. You will never have this sense if you feel hostage to your job. Your sense that you have actively chosen your work, and that you can do something to enhance the experience of your work, is a direct defense against feelings of helplessness and being overwhelmed. And to overcome those feelings is to directly mediate against the factors that result in secondary trauma.

The Skill Domains of the CE-CERT Model

The CE-CERT model (components for enhancing clinician experience and reducing trauma) consist of five skill domains that collectively *enhance our ability to consciously affect autonomic dysregulation.* These skills facilitate what I have called cognitive breathing: inhalation (expecting and allowing stress and strong feelings) and exhalation (allowing intense experiences to come to finish, return to baseline). In short, they are skills to make us better able to allow the natural stress response to rise and fall without our cognitive reactions interrupting that natural, metabolic process.

The CE-CERT model is not comprised merely of concepts. Rather, CE-CERT consists of operationally defined, active skills. After each discussion of concepts, I will provide a map for bridging the concepts into practical skills. Oliver Wendell Holmes described people who were, "...so heaven minded they are of no earthly good". The CE-CERT skills are concrete enough to be of "earthly good". They can be applied in the real stress field of your work. Like any skill, we may struggle at first to acquire facility, but we can get better, and the skills more effortless, as we practice them. Here is a brief overview of the five CE-CERT skills that will comprise the next five chapters. As you leave the familiar world, here is the new territory we are entering:

Experiential Engagement

Experiential engagement refers to the willingness to open up to the aspects of your job that you find the most threatening or the most aversive. It is, in a sentence, learning to avoid avoidance. We have believed—even been taught to believe—that we should fear our feelings. We have learned that we should distract from negative feelings, and that if we have too many strong feelings—sadness, empathy for our clients—that it will cause burnout or compassion fatigue. Most of us—by nature—seek out and attempt to hold on to positive feelings and try to avoid stress and negative feelings. This often extends to avoiding the aspects of our job associated with those feelings. Perhaps we avoid certain activities, perhaps certain client types, perhaps certain emotions, such as grief.

As logical as it is to avoid unpleasant things, fear of unpleasant feelings is irrational. Bad feelings are just bad feelings; they come, and they go. If we were rational, we would fear *not* feeling. Because *not* feeling is the first step toward leaning away from aspects of our job. You think engagement feels dangerous? Try boredom. It's actually under-stimulation that ultimately will kill your career. And it won't feel like boredom—it will feel like too much of the wrong kind of stress and too little of the right kind of stimulation. The first step towards this downward spiral is avoiding the feelings or situations that we find aversive. And leaning away—avoidance—is the first step in the burnout process. In other words, *not* engaging intensity is what burns us out. Experiencing and metabolizing intense feelings or intense situations—perhaps counterintuitively—is what saves us.

The next chapter will describe how to increase experiential engagement. Buddhists describe the aspiration of developing a "soft front and a strong back". In Chapter 2, I will operationalize that concept. How do we willingly open up to things that are difficult for us, or even that threaten us? And how do we maintain the "strong back" to not be overcome by those experiences? In keeping with the three-act structure, Chapter 2 initiates the second act of our story—leaving the world as we know it. If we do this right, our jobs should be adventures. And it won't be an adventure if we aren't willing to accept some feelings of danger.

Decreasing Rumination

Reducing rumination is the practice of letting experiences go. Leaving the past in the past and moving into the next moment. Our brain is "sticky"—because remembering bad experiences is "survival salient", our brain holds onto stressful experiences. We possess the (unfortunate?) ability to conjure and re-conjure events in our minds eye that can re-energize those events ad infinitum. And in this way, a temporary, short-lived event can insert itself into the present moment, contaminating that experience and dominating our evening. Or even our night's sleep.

Re-creating these experiences—having them intrude in our thoughts—is the hallmark of secondary trauma. We can acquire the ability to help our brain to be less sticky, to let those experiences slide into the past. Reducing rumination is the focus of Chapter 3, which defines these skills.

To the degree that you are better able to leave ruminations behind, the quality of your evenings will be more restorative. And, when stress events feel more like discrete, time-limited events than ruin-your-whole-day incidents, you will find it easier to engage difficult experiences without avoidance.

Conscious Narrative

The conscious narrative dimension of the CE-CERT model takes concepts from cognitive approaches and fashions them in the language of narrative. It was Norman Vincent Peale—not the cognitive theorists—who gave us the aphorism "If you change your thoughts you change your world" (Peale, 1956). Or, more specific to the topic of conscious narrative, "If you want to change your job, change the story you are telling about your job".

Although I just quoted Norman Vincent Peale, this is not mere "positive thinking". Cognitive behavioral therapy is not comprised of "just think happy thoughts". Rather, cognitive behavioral therapists actively seek out negative distortions and correct them. Cognitive behavioral therapy is about making our story align more closely to reality; it is not about creating a happy illusion.

The conscious narrative is directing deliberate oversight to the story that we tell ourselves about our work. Because our brain seeks the three-part story in order to resolve stress, we will examine the narratives that we engage in during each of those three acts: before, during, and after a stress event. I have termed these narratives the antecedent, concurrent, and consolidation narratives. By focusing attention to these narratives, we can prime ourselves to open to experience, including difficult experiences. We can talk ourselves through stress in ways that keep us healthy. And we can make meaning out of it all in a way that sustains us over a long career.

Reducing Emotional Labor

The third act of this book, when we "return with the elixir", is the exhale. This is when we let go of the fight. We don't have to work hard or fight dragons anymore. We can make our work easier. The "elixir" with which we are returning is that very realization that we don't have to labor so hard. There are ways the work can carry its own momentum. We can reduce emotional labor when we appreciate that work doesn't only *demand* our energy, it is also a *source* of energy.

The field of occupational psychology has studied emotional labor since the concept was identified in 1983 by sociologist Arlie Hochschild (Hochschild, 1983). Emotional labor refers to the process of managing one's feelings as part of one's job. Since the term was coined, there have been decades of research about the emotional labor of job roles such as sales, medicine, and social work. I will draw from the evidence to develop strategies for reducing the amount of emotional labor it takes to do our work.

Your role requires you to manage your emotions under intense circumstances—and that is hard work. That is why it is all-important that we learn strategies to reduce the amount of emotional labor that our job role requires. If your job isn't going to deplete you over your career, it can't all be unpleasant, exhausting work. The CE-CERT practices will *enhance your experience* and reduce trauma. Skills to reduce emotional labor make our work easier, less effortful. And that has the potential to make our jobs more enjoyable.

Parasympathetic Recovery

CE-CERT challenges you to give up your search for "work–life balance". Don't worry—you can keep those good moments when you are away from work. But if you are going to stop figuratively holding your breath through the workday, then you must learn to breathe while you are at work. CE-CERT isn't only about cognitive breathing; it is about breathing *all day long.*

The sympathetic response is the body's fight-or-flight stress response. This is the inbreath of the cognitive breath. The parasympathetic response is the recovery mechanism—the body's return from sympathetic arousal back to a calm state, back to homeostasis. This is the outbreath.

Chapter 8 will provide strategies for creating whitespace during the workday that allows us to breathe. We need space to develop a breathing rhythm during the day, so we aren't contracting, holding our breath. Sure, it is hard when your days feel chockablock with tasks and stressors. But it can and must be done. And when you have accomplished the creation of this sense of some breathing room, it will be easier to flow between your workday and your home life. And then it will be easier to give up the notion of a rigid boundary between work and "life".

Each of the CE-CERT skill domains are components of the cognitive breath—willingness to inhale fully, and the ability to exhale fully. The CE-CERT skills facilitate this natural process that our body has evolved to perform. We allow the full stress/recovery process to complete itself without our emotions, reactions, or cognitions getting in the way.

When we can do that, our jobs become easier. We can do this for a whole career...

References

Bober, T. & Regehr, C. (2006). Strategies for reducing secondary or vicarious trauma: Do they work? *Brief Treatment and Crisis Intervention, 6*(1), 1.

Caraballo, J. M. (2014). *The essence of a young poet.* Bloomington, IN: Xlibris.

Carey, D., Helford, H., Graham, C. (Writers), & Cohen, G. (Director). (1998, September 30). In Ramada Da Vida. [Television series episode]. In R. Baker (Producer), *The Drew Carey Show.* Burbank, ABC.

Carney, J., Donovan, R., Yurdin, M., Starr, R., Pernell-Arnold, A., & Bromberg, E. M. (1993). Incidence of burnout among New York City intensive case managers: Summary of findings. *Psychosocial Rehabilitation Journal, 16*(4), 25.

Cieslak, R., Shoji, K., Douglas, A., Melville, E., Luszczynska, A., & Benight, C. C. (2014). A meta-analysis of the relationship between job burnout and secondary traumatic stress among workers with indirect exposure to trauma. *Psychological Services, 11*(1), 75.

Conrad, D., & Kellar-Guenther, Y. (2006). Compassion fatigue, burnout, and compassion satisfaction among Colorado child protection workers. *Child Abuse & Neglect, 30*(10), 1071–1080.

Craig, C. D., & Sprang, G. (2010). Compassion satisfaction, compassion fatigue, and burnout in a national sample of trauma treatment therapists. *Anxiety, Stress, & Coping, 23*(3), 319–339.

Etzion, D. (2003). Annual vacation: Duration of relief from job stressors and burnout. *Anxiety, Stress, and Coping, 16*(2), 213–226.

Fagin, L., Carson, J., Leary, J., De Villiers, N., Bartlett, H., O'Malley, P., & Brown, D. (1996). Stress, coping and burnout in mental health nurses: Findings from three research studies. *International Journal of Social Psychiatry, 42*(2), 102–111.

Fernando III, A. T., & Consedine, N. S. (2014). Beyond compassion fatigue: The transactional model of physician compassion. *Journal of Pain and Symptom Management, 48*(2), 289–298.

Gregory, A. (2015). Yoga and mindfulness program: The effects on compassion fatigue and compassion satisfaction in social workers. *Journal of Religion & Spirituality in Social Work: Social Thought, 34*(4), 372–393.

Hochschild, A. R. (1983). *The managed heart: Commercialization of human feeling.* Berkeley: University of California Press.

Iglesias, M. E. L., de Bengoa Vallejo, R. B., & Fuentes, P. S. (2010). The relationship between experiential avoidance and burnout syndrome in critical care nurses: A cross-sectional questionnaire survey. *International Journal of Nursing Studies, 47*(1), 30–37.

Kim, H. (2011). Job conditions, unmet expectations, and burnout in public child welfare workers: How different from other social workers?. *Children and Youth Services Review, 33*(2), 358–367.

Klimecki, O., & Singer, T. (2012). Empathic distress fatigue rather than compassion fatigue? Integrating findings from empathy research in psychology and social neuroscience. In B. Oakley, A. Knafo, G. Madhavan, & D. S. Wilson (Eds.), *Pathological altruism* (pp. 368–383). Oxford: Oxford University Press.

Kroska, E. B., Calarge, C., O'Hara, M. W., Deumic, E., & Dindo, L. (2017). Burnout and depression in medical students: Relations with avoidance and disengagement. *Journal of Contextual Behavioral Science, 6*(4), 404–408.

Levine, P. A., & Frederick, A. (1997). *Waking the tiger: Healing trauma: The innate capacity to transform overwhelming experiences.* Berkeley, California: North Atlantic Books.

Luken, M., & Sammons, A. (2016). Systematic review of mindfulness practice for reducing job burnout. *American Journal of Occupational Therapy, 70*(2), 1–10.

Maslach, C. & Schaufeli, W. B. (1993). Historical and conceptual development of burnout. *Professional burnout: Recent developments in theory and research* (vol. 12, pp. 1–16).

Naidoo, L. J., DeCriscio, A., Bily, H., Manipella, A., Ryan, M., & Youdim, J. (2012). The 2 × 2 model of goal orientation and burnout: The role of approach–avoidance dimensions in predicting burnout. *Journal of Applied Social Psychology*, *42*(10), 2541–2563.

O'Connor, K., Neff, D. M., & Pitman, S. (2018). Burnout in mental health professionals: A systematic review and meta-analysis of prevalence and determinants. *European Psychiatry*, *53*, 74–99.

Peale, N. V. (1956). *The power of positive thinking*. Englewood Cliffs, NJ: Prentice-Hall.

Polman, R., Borkoles, E., & Nicholls, A. R. (2010). Type D personality, stress, and symptoms of burnout: The influence of avoidance coping and social support. *British Journal of Health Psychology*, *15*(3), 681–696.

Raga, S. (March 14, 2017). *Florence Chadwick, the woman who conquered the English Channel*. Retrieved from https://www.mentalfloss.com/article/93072/retrobituaries-florence-chadwick-woman-who-conquered-english-channel.

Riley, K. E., Park, C. L., Wilson, A., Sabo, A. N., Antoni, M. H., Braun, T. D. & Cope, S.(2017). Improving physical and mental health in frontline mental health care providers: Yoga-based stress management versus cognitive behavioral stress management. *Journal of Workplace Behavioral Health*, *32*(1), 26–48.

Sheldon, K. M., & Lyubomirsky, S. (2006). Achieving sustainable gains in happiness: Change your actions, not your circumstances. *Journal of Happiness Studies*, *7*(1), 55–86.

Söderfeldt, M., Söderfeldt, B., & Warg, L. E. (1995). Burnout in social work. *Social Work*, *40*(5), 638–646.

Sprang, G., Craig, C., & Clark, J. (2011). Secondary traumatic stress and burnout in child welfare workers: A comparative analysis of occupational distress across professional groups. *Child Welfare*, *90*(6), 149–168.

Sullivan, P. A., & Nashman, H. W. (1999). Burnout 25 years later: A review of risk factors and work demands. In *Research quarterly for exercise and sport* (Vol. 70, No. 1, pp. A47). Reston, Va: American Alliance of Health Physical Education and Dance.

Strand, C. (September 29, 2011). *Tricycle*. Green Koans Case 60: Dōgen's To-Do List. Retrieved from https://tricycle.org/trikedaily/green-koans-case-60-dogens-to-do-list/.

Tamura, L. J., Guy, J. D., Brady, J. L., & Grace, C. (1995). Psychotherapists' management of confidentiality, burnout and affiliation needs: A national survey. *Psychotherapy in Private Practice*, *13*(2), 1–17.

Van Der Ploeg, H. M., Van Leeuwen, J. J., & Kwee, M. G. (1990). Burnout among Dutch psychotherapists. *Psychological Reports*, *67*(1), 107–112.

Van Hook, M. P., Rothenberg, M., Fisher, K., Elias, A., Helton, S., Williams, S., Pena, S., & Gregory, A. (2008). Conference Report, NACSW, 1–18.

Van Mol, M. M., Kompanje, E. J., Benoit, D. D., Bakker, J., & Nijkamp, M. D. (2015). The prevalence of compassion fatigue and burnout among healthcare professionals in intensive care units: A systematic review. *PloS One*, *10*(8), e0136955.

Volpe, U., Luciano, M., Palumbo, C., Sampogna, G., Del Vecchio, V., & Fiorillo, A. (2014). Risk of burnout among early career mental health professionals. *Journal of Psychiatric and Mental Health Nursing*, *21*(9), 774–781.

Wagaman, M. A., Geiger, J. M., Shockley, C., & Segal, E. A. (2015). The role of empathy in burnout, compassion satisfaction, and secondary traumatic stress among social workers. *Social Work*, *60*(3), 201–209.

Wilkinson, C. B., Infantolino, Z. P., & Wacha-Montes, A. (2017). Evidence-based practice as a potential solution to burnout in university counseling center clinicians. *Psychological Services*, *14*(4), 543.

Zhang, Y. Y., Han, W. L., Qin, W., Yin, H. X., Zhang, C. F., Kong, C., & Wang, Y. L. (2018). Extent of compassion satisfaction, compassion fatigue and burnout in nursing: A meta-analysis. *Journal of Nursing Management*, *26*(7), 810–819.

Section II

Leaving the Ordinary World: Our Quest Begins

2 Entering the Woods at the Darkest Place—Experiential Engagement

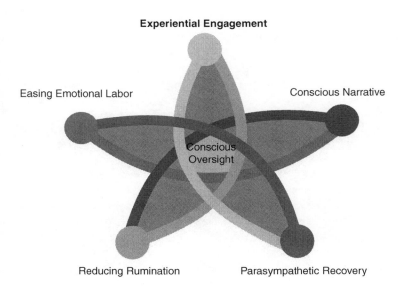

He who binds to himself a joy

Does the winged life destroy;

But he who kisses the joy as it flies

Lives in Eternity's sunrise.

William Blake (1804)

I: The Challenge

Dealing with secondary traumatic stress shouldn't be too difficult. All you have to do is minimize exposure to traumatizing scenes or feelings and maximize rewarding experiences, right? Employing the same glib logic, job satisfaction should also be easy: just minimize the unpleasant part of your job—or just don't think about it—and maximize the pleasurable parts of your work. Just like your grandmother used to sing to you, you just have to accentuate the positive and eliminate the negative. Well, it turns out that this was strikingly bad advice.

In this chapter, I am throwing down a gauntlet. I am challenging you—in the context of your job—to gather your courage to "enter the woods at the darkest place". Most "experts" dispensing advice to trauma workers will suggest that your job is already too hard, and you should do more to care for yourself. This isn't that book, and that approach isn't based on any research that I have seen. The idea that we need to minimize our negative feelings and care for ourselves more is one of the sacred mountains of our profession. I'm going to suggest—and provide evidence—that something else entirely is indicated. The positive moments that we want cannot always be *pursued*—we must allow them to *ensue*. And they will ensue, as long as we open ourselves to the hard thing. Here's the headline of this chapter: the royal highway to job satisfaction leads through the most dissatisfying elements of your job.

Joseph Campbell said the second act of the hero's journey begins when the hero/heroine leaves the safety and creature comforts of home and decides to "enter the woods at the darkest place". This is a fine place to begin the second act of our story. And herein lies the evidence-based message that delivers a wedgie to that sacred mountain known as "self-care": to a very real degree, the extent to which you enjoy your job—and can sustain in your job for the long haul—will be determined by your willingness to accept this challenge of opening up *to the most aversive*—anxiety-inducing, unpleasant, monotonous, or sad—aspects of your job. These are the dark places in the forest through which we must pass. That gets pretty close to the opposite of the "self-care" shibboleth. But the challenge to enter these places aligns with the research evidence: there is a direct correlation between your openness to the *discomfort* caused by your work and your *enjoyment* of your work.

II: Experiential Engagement: Avoiding Avoidance

The degree to which you like your work—or the degree to which you would like any job—is determined by how many pleasurable moments you have in that role. That makes obvious sense. But allow me to state a seemingly trite observation: we can only experience those pleasurable and meaningful moments by *feeling* sensations that we describe as pleasure or a sense of purpose, by *a felt sense* of pleasure or meaning. In other words, in order to love our jobs deeply, we must be capable of feeling deeply. The degree to which we have access to our feelings sets the stage for enjoying our work—and yes, for hating our work.

I will use a specific scenario: imagine that I am anticipating meeting with a client who was hostile and defensive in my previous interactions. I fully expect that this meeting will be unpleasant. I expect to be insulted and thwarted in my helping efforts. There are a variety of ways that I can respond as I anticipate this undesirable task: I can avoid the meeting entirely (tell my supervisor I don't do well with this type of client and request that she be transferred to another provider); or I can meet with the client and suppress my feelings of fear and defensiveness when she is hostile toward me. Afterward, I will turn down the volume of my feelings, both to myself and my co-workers, as I proclaim, "I'm fine, no worries".

Both of these responses represent experiential avoidance—either physically avoiding the circumstance entirely, or avoiding the unpleasant emotions that result from the interaction with the client. Perhaps you have an undeclared strategy of attempting to minimize how often you have to experience such negative exchanges. That way, your job will become more enjoyable more often. Maybe someone else who may be less provoked by this client can deal with her, while you can attend to clients more in your wheelhouse.

In the rest of our lives, the logic makes sense. Making a choice between going to a good movie or enduring an unnecessary root canal isn't a difficult decision—of course, we want to avoid one and seek out the other. But if we employ this selective strategy in our inner world of emotions—trying to avoid negative feelings, but at the same time trying to fully experience the positive feelings—not only will we fail, but we will also set the stage for disengaging from our work. Most of our work is neither particularly dreadful nor particularly satisfying. With apologies to Johnny Mercer, the fact is, you spend most of your job day "messin' with Mr. In-between"—most of your work is neutral in terms of emotional load.

Sam Keen was demonstrably correct when he said, "We can't choose *what* to feel. We can only choose *whether* to feel" (1991). Emotions, it seems, are an all-or-nothing, dampen-the-bad-feelings, dampen-the-good-feelings proposition. Our feeling pathways—maintaining a "soft front"—must be equally open to both pleasurable and aversive feelings if our goal is to find pleasure and reward in our work. As the comedienne Paula Poundstone put it, "Eat the pecan pie. Don't like nuts? Spit 'em out. But the rest of the pie is too good to miss".

This makes a puzzle out of the apparently self-evident formula: pleasurable experiences at work = I enjoy my job. The evidence is that it isn't so straight-forward as that. There is a great deal of research that confirms that the reason you experience pleasurable events at work is because you have opened yourself to the *aversive* aspects of your work. Donaldson-Feilder and Bond came to an interesting conclusion in their research on acceptance and emotional intelligence:

> People who are more emotionally willing to experience negative emotional experiences enjoy better mental health and do better at work over time. The effect is significantly greater than the effects of job satisfaction or emotional intelligence. (Donaldson-Feilder & Bond, 2004)

Allow that to land for a moment: one of the single most important determinants of your level of enjoyment in your job—and your mental health in that job—is your willingness to experience the parts of your job *that you don't like*. That is why I am challenging you to "enter the woods at the darkest place". Are you willing to look squarely at the aspects of your job that you try to avoid, and to open yourself to those activities, and to those emotions? Are you willing to enter the woods at precisely the place that you have been avoiding? In trauma work, this is not a trivial challenge. These experiences, these images, these emotions may be very intense and very frightening. It isn't hyperbole to compare opening to those experiences as comparable to "entering the woods at the darkest place".

Emotional Avoidance Is a Factor in Secondary Trauma

The relationship between avoidance and burnout became very clear as soon as researchers disabused themselves of the idea that burnout is caused by "over-commitment to a cause", (Iglesias et al., 2010; Kroska et al., 2017; Naidoo et al., 2012; Polman et al., 2010; Vilardaga et al., 2011). The correlation between a person engaging in avoidance behaviors and risk for burnout is well established in the research. When your engagement is high, you will experience high amounts of vigor and commitment to your work. These things naturally occur together. When you are avoiding key parts of your job, energy and commitment to the work will diminish.

The research on secondary trauma is awaiting the same kind of enlightenment that occurred in burnout research. Heretofore, experiential avoidance has been viewed as a symptom of, rather than a contributing cause of, secondary trauma. But this hole in the research quickly closes when we remind ourselves that secondary trauma is a form of trauma. And in the trauma treatment field, we have established—to the point of exhausting—the fact that exposure (the exact opposite of avoidance) is the treatment of choice. Exposure therapy is, in effect, also learning how to avoid avoidance. If a person with a trauma history avoids memories and feelings associated with a traumatic event, we expect the sequelae of the trauma—mood disturbance, anxiety, intrusive images— to continue unabated. Persons with trauma history also must be challenged to enter the woods at the darkest place. In trauma treatment, we call it exposure therapy.

We don't expect our clients with trauma history to get well until they do the therapeutic work of dealing with their memories and feelings. And in the same way, avoiding aspects of your work that are aversive—or feelings that are unpleasant—is an ineffective strategy for preserving your well-being on the job. Your ability to enjoy your job cannot be expanded unless your ability to fully open to the undesirable aspects of your job increases.

Avoidance Leads to Secondary Trauma and Burnout

Let's return to the example: I am deciding what to do in anticipation of meeting with a hostile, defensive client. I decide to meet with her and—as I expected—she rejects my helping efforts and is angry and insulting towards me. I maintain a professional demeanor with her, speak to her in a reassuring, calm manner, and respond to every criticism as if it is valid feedback. In other words, I am exemplary in my professionalism. But it is exhausting to suppress my feelings of defensiveness, hurt, or anger. This suppression is the very embodiment of emotional labor (which I will discuss in Chapter 5). I am acutely aware of her anger and defensiveness, but I don't pay attention to the defensiveness and anger that I am experiencing. I act opposite to my genuine feelings in order to maintain a professional demeanor. After the encounter, I minimize the level of provocation that I experience within myself ("That's what I signed up for") and with others ("No worries—I'm fine".)

By suppressing strong feelings, I have interrupted the metabolization of these emotions (anger and fear). Because the process has been interrupted, the energy of those emotions isn't fully expended, allowing those feelings to exist in an inchoate form that can recycle almost indefinitely. The experience itself was unpleasant—and because of the emotional hangover that carries on for hours afterwards—my work becomes a little more unpleasant. This, in turn, may lead to future avoidance of this kind of experience. Dampening down the intensity of the unwelcome feelings requires that I distance myself from the feelings—I numb my ability to feel.

As I approach work in my newly defended self, I have a slightly more negative view of my duties because I am carrying over those aversive experiences. I come to work with a new sense of dread. My ability to feel is dampened down (both good and bad) because I don't want to experience those uncomfortable feelings—anger and fear—again. I wish to avoid more negative experiences, so I physically and emotionally employ escape strategies. As I avoid intensity—because I want to avoid intensely negative feelings—I am certain to feel less engagement in my work. At some point—sooner or later—I will say that I am "burned out". It is as if, as one essayist put it, "we lock ourselves in a panic room and cut ourselves off from the ten thousand joys and sorrows…"

The life of fire fighters has been described as "long moments of boredom punctuated by brief moments of sheer terror". We create the same dynamic as we engage in experiential avoidance in our jobs. We disengage from unpleasant tasks in order to protect our feeling state, but as we begin to lean away from the intensity of our job, we experience more numbness and under-stimulation. Boredom that will be punctuated by those moments of the "terror" of the situations that we are unable to escape.

The poet Mark Nepo (2011) says it this way: "It's like wearing gloves every time we touch something, and then, forgetting we chose to put them on, we complain that nothing feels quite real. Our challenge each day is not to get dressed to face the world but to unglove ourselves so that the doorknob feels cold and the car handle feels wet..."

A study done by Matthew Fish at East Carolina University caught my eye because the conclusions contradicted what I thought I knew about video games. In his (small) study, adolescents with anxiety disorders who were on SSRIs, and who needed supplementation with a second treatment, were sorted into one group that received a second medication. The other group added casual video games to their routine four times a week for 30–35 minutes in lieu of a second medication. The results that Fish obtained were that the video game group did significantly *better* on measures of anxiety and depression that the medication group. That's right—in this study, video games were added to SSRI medications and successfully reduced anxiety and depression better than did a second medication (Fish, 2014).

But wait a minute—isn't video game use associated with depression and anxiety in adolescents? Indeed, many studies have shown exactly this association (Marchica et al., 2020; Milani et al., 2019; Nguyen & Landau, 2019). But Fish's finding has been replicated in many studies that not only looked at associations between video game use and depression/anxiety symptoms, but also examined *why* the adolescents were playing video games. And what they find is consistent: using video games to distract oneself from stress is correlated with psychological symptoms (Von Der Heiden et al., 2019). Fish had his subjects use video games in a dose-controlled, intentional way. And when the adolescents did that—as opposed to using video games mindlessly to distract from the feelings they don't want to deal with—video game usage is associated with positive outcomes.

Video games don't cause depression or anxiety. Video games don't alleviate depression or anxiety. But avoiding avoidance—experiential engagement—does result in better mental health. And better job health.

If you avoid a feeling or experience, those feelings aren't really evaded; they are merely dampened. The energy of the emotion will linger, and the emotion that we were attempting to escape will incubate and actually increase in duration. The anxiety that we add through our avoidance may actually intensify the feelings.

Traci Brimhall (2018) quotes her young son's wisdom about how this energy dynamic operates. She described asking her four-year-old son what his favorite part of living was. She reported that his answer—surprisingly—was crying. When she asked him to explain, he said it was because it felt so good to stop when he was happy again. That is cognitive breathing embodied: opening to the sadness because it clears the way to happiness.

Opening the door to anxiety because it clears the way for calmness. Opening the door to fear because it clears the way for feelings of well-being.

Our goal is to allow unpleasant emotions to be fully metabolized so the energy is expended without producing secondary trauma. Imagine that a powerful, negative emotion has a discrete amount of metabolic energy—let's say 100 "feeling units". In their primary form, emotions do, in fact, have a discrete amount of energy and have a limited natural history. Neuroanatomist Jill Bolte Taylor (2008) describes these feelings as 90 second chemical events—90 seconds! Imagine that you can allocate the 100 feeling units over a 24-hour period. You must allocate all 100 units in the rules of this thought experiment. And, in real life, you do have to allocate all of the "feeling energy" of an emotion.

You might allocate those units by trying to experience them at a low level to keep them tolerable. Maybe, you believe that keeping the feelings at a "slow boil" will prevent them from overwhelming you. Or, maybe you are attempting to not experience those feelings at all, but they nonetheless break through throughout the day. The burn rate for those slow-boiling feelings might look something like this:

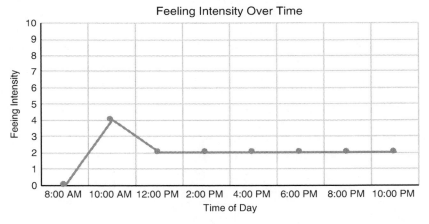

Notice two things about the burn rate of feelings illustrated in the chart: although the intensity of feeling is relatively low, the feeling is affecting your experiences throughout the day—even if at a reduced level; and note that at 10:00 PM, the "energy burn" is still occurring. Although the intensity of the negative feeling never rose above "4" and stayed at a low simmer of "2" the rest of the day, it was still present at 10:00 PM. In other words, you are still emotionally experiencing the event as you end your day hours after the stressful event.

Now consider the burn rate of the same 100 feeling units if you open fully to the experience in real-time:

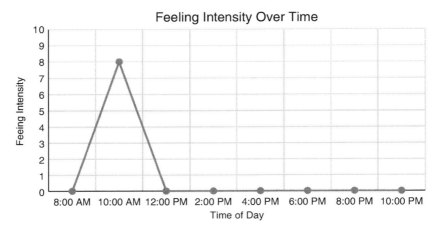

In this allocation of the feeling units, at 10:00 AM—the time of the unpleasant interaction with my client—I am feeling very uncomfortable. I feel the emotions at full burn. Put any label on the feeling—it could be any or all of the emotions that are experienced as unpleasant—anger, confused, afraid, hurt, sad. This isn't enjoyable—I rate my discomfort at an 8 on a 10-point scale. But now notice the burn rate of the feeling units—by lunch I am back in my "green zone", my baseline state. By the time I am home with my family that evening, the discrete chemical event has expended its metabolic energy, and I can have a good evening.

This scenario is only a thought experiment, but it demonstrates a neurochemical reality. As Bolt Taylor demonstrated, that neurochemical event is a brief expenditure of chemical energy. An additional factor we must account for, however, is that after the initial unpleasant event, we can rekindle the chemical process by re-creating it in our brain. When we do that, we reproduce the chemical event, and we will respond in the same way we did in the original experience. That is why, in the next chapter, we will address how to reduce our tendency to ruminate—to reproduce these events beyond the initial experience. For now, we will retain our focus on the primary event, and our engagement with that event.

Susan Cain, in her book *Quiet* (2012), describes a fascinating study conducted by Judith Grob as part of her doctoral dissertation (Grob, 2009). Grob had subjects look at disgusting images while expressing their emotion of disgust, or when they were told to not express emotion, or while they were holding a pencil in their mouths (unknowingly expressing a half-smile). In other words, one group was experiencing the emotion of disgust, while two groups were suppressing their natural disgust. When she had those three groups complete word-completion tasks, the two groups who suppressed their facial expressions offered more negative words (e.g., gross) than the non-suppressors (e.g., grass). The suppressors also performed more poorly on memory tasks.

Grob and others have used this study to examine the role of facial expressions and emotion. But I see something else here as well. Consider for a moment what happened during this study: by tricking you into suppressing your expression of disgust, the experience of disgust later "leaks out" into you seeing GR_SS as *gross* rather than *grass*. Your disgust—which hadn't been allowed full expression—leaked into another experience. That psychic energy demanded expression and contaminated the next experience. But when the full expression of disgust was allowed—by not avoiding your disgust—the feelings expended their energy fully. GR_SS was seen as "grass", not "gross". The disgust had completely run its course.

Grob's study is just one drop in the sea of research that demonstrates the negative effects associated with emotion suppression and experiential avoidance. Intense events initiate a neuro- and physiological chemical sequence that cannot be stopped or hoarded. As with time, we can only decide how to spend this energy. Do we allow the full and immediate expression—and exhaustion—of this energy, or do we dampen its expression into a longer-lived but low-level event? In other words, do we allow the fever of this stressor to break, or do we resign ourselves to a low-grade fever that can go on indefinitely? You don't get a choice to simply not experience whatever it is that you are avoiding. You can experience it directly and immediately, or you can, as Matt Hooper told the mayor in the movie *Jaws*: "...ignore this particular problem until it swims up and bites you on the ass..."

Wisdom Both Ancient and Empirical

Although the principle of "avoiding avoidance" may be new language, it certainly isn't a new idea. The wisdom about not trying to enhance happiness by escaping "suffering" is ancient and occurs in a variety of belief systems and vocabularies. But it is significant to our modern worldview that this traditional wisdom is also confirmed by empirical research. This isn't just "wisdom", it is empirical fact.

The concept of opening to our experience is found throughout ancient Buddhism and the writings of both ancient and contemporary Buddhist thinkers:

> "Don't run away from things that are unpleasant in order to embrace things that are pleasant. Put your hands in the earth. Face the difficulties and grow new happiness".
>
> —Thích Nhất Hạnh (1999)

"Hold the sadness and pain of samsara in your heart and at the same time the power and vision of the Great Eastern Sun. Then the warrior can make a proper cup of tea".

—Chögyam Trungpa Rinpoche (2001)

"Clearly recognizing what is happening inside us, and regarding what we see with an open, kind and loving heart, is what I call Radical Acceptance. If we are holding back from any part of our experience, if our heart shuts out any part of who we are and what we feel, we are fueling the fears and feelings of separation that sustain the trance of unworthiness. Radical Acceptance directly dismantles the very foundations of this trance".

—Tara Brach (2003)

And from the Psalms:

"But they delight in the way things are
and keep their hearts open, day and night.
They are like trees planted near flowing rivers,
which bear fruit when they are ready.
Their leaves will not fall or wither.
Everything they do will succeed".

And poets such as William Blake (Mitchell, 1994):

"And under every grief and pine
runs a joy with silken twine".

Experiencing things the way things are—the good and the bad, the enjoyable and the painful. Or, as Joseph Campbell said it, being willing to "participate joyfully in the sorrows of the world". Or even, in the current vernacular of youth, being willing to "embrace the suck".

The focus on opening to experience—both negative and positive—is based upon more than age-old aphorisms or current clichés. To borrow a phrase from Ariel Levy, "Religion, art, literature, and Oprah" have all established the importance of opening to the unpleasant aspects of experience. And we can add a wealth of empirical evidence to that list. I take immense pleasure in the fact that the same advice that poets and sages such as Rumi give for us to open ourselves to all difficult guests can also be described in scientific and neurophysiological terms. The poetic concept has been established with empirical research. This large body of research confirms what "religion, art, literature, and Oprah" have suggested: the benefits of opening, and the danger of avoidance as a strategy for emotional protection.

Steven Hayes is the principal architect of Acceptance and Commitment Therapy (ACT). ACT is one of the treatment approaches known as the third wave models because, like other third wave models, it integrates ancient wisdom and modern empirical research. Acceptance (the A in ACT) is a foundational concept within the model, and therefore a large portion of the model includes experiential willingness as we describe it here. One ACT mantra is "if you're not willing to have it, you will". This is a pithy way of getting at the energy dynamic of emotions that is baked into CE-CERT. If you aren't willing to *experience* an emotion, that emotion will linger and will leak out in the form of general job unhappiness, or even in extreme forms such as panic attacks.

Dr. Hayes has identified—and conducted—considerable research that supports the importance of experiential willingness to emotional well-being. For instance, he cites research demonstrating that acceptance increases pain tolerance (Hayes et al., 1999); improves self-management of chronic disease (Gregg 2004); decreases panic (Karekla et al., 2004); reduces post-trauma in adult child abuse victims (Marx & Sloan, 2005); and reduces depression (Hayes et al., 2004).

In full alignment with Hayes's research, the totality of this area of social science research compellingly establishes three facts: 1) managing unpleasant feelings through escape strategies rather than the full experience of those feelings is a psychological vulnerability (Kashdan et al., 2006); 2) in contrast, emotional openness is a quality that is strongly associated with mental well-being; and 3) exposure to anxiety-inducing stimuli decreases anxiety and increases well-being (Powers & Emmelkamp, 2008).

So, let's sum up the case and focus it specifically to you and the work that you do: if you are emotionally open to the parts of your job that you don't enjoy—and open to fully experience the feelings that occur during those events—these emotions will be "metabolized" and short-lived. You will be healthier and happier in your job.

Our task now is to take this "heaven-minded" wisdom and make of it some "earthly good". How can we become more skillful at opening to experience?

Experiential Engagement: Skills for Developing a Soft Front and Strong Back

In Chapter 1, I noted that each skill domain begins with defining a target—setting an intention. How do I establish a "soft front" that is open to aversive experience when it feels like every cell in my body seems to want to avoid it? How do I stand my ground when that mountain lion is 20 feet away, even if I believe that not running away is my best strategy? Maintaining a soft front requires that we also have a strong back. It is the courage described by Rilke: "Let everything happen to you: beauty and terror. Just keep going..." The strong back is the conviction that, as Rilke says, "No feeling is final" (n.d.). Opening up to our most dreaded feelings isn't work for cowards. But then, neither is trauma work for cowards.

Step 1: Setting an Intention

Defining your target for enhancing experiential engagement may necessitate a paradigm shift. Perhaps you have been hoping that something about your work will change so that it becomes easier to tolerate. Perhaps you have resigned yourself to a lower level of job satisfaction, or a higher level of job distress, than you initially signed on for. If either of these describe—or even partially describe you—then passive hoping or resignation must be exchanged for an active target. More specifically, I invite you to this challenge: "How can I become skillful in ways that allow me to fully experience all that this job demands of me"? Instead of passively hoping for your work to change, what is it like to consider how you might become skillful enough to contend with the demands being made of you? Not unhealthy or unreasonable demands made by an unhealthy organization, mind you, but the inherent demands of your appropriate role as a trauma therapist.

I introduced this chapter by challenging you to enter the woods at the darkest place—at *your* darkest place. What is that place? What is that thing that you avoid? What is the client situation—or type—that you dread the most? What is the activity that the job requires you to do that is the most aversive to you? What emotion is the hardest for you to allow yourself to feel, to express, and to metabolize? If you are having a hard time identifying a target, go to the self-audit at the end of this chapter and reflect on those questions.

The bullseye of our target for experiential engagement looks like this:

1. "I am open and willing to experience discomfort, anxiety, sadness, and other uncomfortable emotions—and the situations that evoke them".
2. "I am able to notice and acknowledge my feelings".
3. "I allow difficult feelings to run their course without stopping them".

Our target for this domain can be stated simply: we want to feel whatever arises from the work we do as trauma workers. To feel it, and to feel it through... not to feel less, but—counterintuitively—to feel *more*. Our intention is, as William James put it, "The whole staying and excitement".

Step 2: Willingness

Margaret Mohrmann is Professor Emerita of Pediatrics, Medical Education, and Religious Studies at the University of Virginia. When delivering the keynote address of a medical school white coat ceremony some years ago, she made the point about opening to the pain of the work in eloquent terms:

> Not only are you going to be touching patients soon; you're also going to be listening to them. You're going to be privileged to hear first-hand the stories people tell about their lives, about their afflictions and their strengths. These will be fragile, often painful stories, the sort of stories that are told only to people who can be trusted to hold them gently and use them rightly...
>
> You are becoming *now* someone set apart to receive special knowledge. Not just the kind of knowledge that you're really excited about learning, about diseases and their causes and treatments. You will also receive knowledge you may not want to have—about how difficult and painful life is for some people, about what people are capable of doing to each other and to themselves, about how people your own age, or your parents' age, or your children's age can suffer and die...
>
> You have to allow yourself to be moved by them, to be changed. When the time comes that you feel tempted to say what too many doctors for too long have said, as though it were true, "I cannot survive this vocation if I let myself get close to my patients"—at that very time I hope you will remember what I'm saying now: "You cannot survive this vocation—cannot endure it, cannot enjoy it, especially cannot do it well—if you do not allow yourself to get close to your patients". If you do not allow yourself to be truly moved by what they tell you and show you, by their awful sufferings and their remarkable recoveries, by their lives and by their deaths.
>
> I very much want you to understand today, if you have any doubts and over against what some others will probably tell you, that having your heart broken by your patients day after day will not kill you. It will not burn you out, or turn you into a cynic, or send you to business school. It is the *un*broken heart, the heart hidden away, secure behind its white coat, that cannot survive a career in medicine, because it will not have the capacity to hold what must be held at the center of good doctoring. It may sound paradoxical to you now, but I tell you truly that it is there, at the center of good doctoring where the broken hearts live, that you will find the great and enduring joy of professing medicine. (M. Mohrmann, personal communication, April 20, 2020)

Dr. Mohrmann was speaking to medical students, but everything she said applies to trauma workers. You also "are privileged to hear firsthand the stories people tell about their lives—their afflictions and about their strengths..." You, as a trauma therapist, also possess a special knowledge. That knowledge includes the things you want to know—trauma treatment interventions, the effect that trauma has on the brain. But that knowledge also includes exposure to painful facts—how human beings are damaged by trauma, and the capability of some broken humans to commit real harm to other humans, even innocent children. You will see and know things that you cannot un-know. You, like those doctors-to-be, are also in a role that will bring you suffering. You also will be tempted to put emotional space between you and your client's suffering. Your role requires either that you be hardened by the stories, or that you will have your heart broken often.

Willingness is the second step toward experiential engagement. Now it is time for a gut-check: are you willing to have your heart broken day after day?

The "strong back" aspect of experiential engagement maintaining confidence that—as Dr. Morhmann said—having your heart broken day after day will not kill you. It will save you. The point that she makes in poetic terms about the "heart having the capacity to hold what must be held" ... relates to how your willingness to experience heartbreak will save you.

In a very real and concrete way, as you stand your ground during strong emotions and difficult situations, those situations metabolize quickly and your need to avoid is reduced. As you—like Traci Brimhall's four-year-old son—have repeated experiences of realizing "how good it feels when it's done, and you're happy again"—your capacity grows. You will come to trust how time-limited—and tolerable—these experiences are. And how good it feels when "you are happy again". When you avoid the same experiences, on the other hand, your world contracts.

Laura van Dernoot Lipski, in her book *Trauma Stewardship*, provides a profile of Harry Spence, who, among his many roles, served as the Commissioner of the Massachusetts Department of Social Services. In that profile, Spence, during a one-hour training that he conducts with all new social workers, trains that the most important decision that they will make as social workers is "...the decision around what you are going to do with the pain of this work" (van Dernoot Lipsky & Burk, 2009).

That is a profound decision. What are you going to do with the pain that arises in your work? You have answered this question, but you probably didn't realize it. Take a moment now to consider how your actions on the job have answered this question. What have you been doing with the pain (or anxiety, or fear, sadness, or whatever form that pain takes) that arises in your work? Have you been avoiding it or tamping it down, trying to make it less intense? Have you been throwing sugar cookies as fast as you can, so the wolves won't pounce? When you ask yourself the question plainly, "What have I been doing with the pain that arises in my work?", there really are only two possible answers: "I have been trying to get away from the pain"; or "I have been feeling the pain". The decision you made will lead to either "I am going to armor up" or "I am going to unglove".

I have fully demonstrated why the first option—"I'm going to armor up" is a bad decision. Not only is it going to fail (if you're not willing to have it, you will...), but it is also going to lessen your job satisfaction and worsen job stress over time. When we reflect explicitly on this question, "What am I going to do with the pain that arises in this work?", there is only one sensible answer: "I'm going to feel it". Feelings must be felt. Knowing this, I can reduce my natural reactiveness by priming my willingness to feel it fully and in the moment, and to feel it through until the distress is metabolized. And for most of us, that will be a significant change.

Reflect upon your current level of willingness—and compare it to where you would like to be. Are you willing to sit with your client's—and your own—pain without trying to escape it? Are you willing to get better at opening to that pain rather than shutting down or getting away? Even before you know *how* to do this, are you *willing* to open that soft front?

Step 3: Noticing

Trauma therapists do emotion work—we work with feelings. Emotion work is another way of describing the therapeutic enterprise. Yes, we call it the "talking cure", but what we are really describing—the center of this work—is emotions and awareness of emotions. Perhaps the most foundational of all of our therapeutic strategies is the question "How did that make you feel?"

Because of the emphasis on feelings in psychotherapy, it strikes me as a paradox that—in my observation—therapists aren't particularly aware of their own feelings. Perhaps, because of our laser-focus on the feelings of our clients, we haven't turned that same awareness towards our own feelings. Perhaps we have intentionally focused away from our feelings in order to maintain a professional, impassive demeanor. We may have even been trained to focus away from our own feelings. Maybe the crush of job demands simply doesn't seem to offer the space to stop and reflect upon our own emotions. Or perhaps some of us—due to our own avoidant natures—want our clients to do our feeling work for us rather than experiencing these feelings ourselves.

Regardless of why we focus away from our own feelings, this unawareness—intentional or unintended—becomes a change target for experiential engagement. If we are going to fully experience our feelings, we must notice them. And in some cases, this may be a profound change from what you are presently doing—or not doing, to be more precise. Before you can feel better, you must get better at noticing *what* you are feeling.

I recall doing clinical supervision with a new child therapist who was caring for a young boy whose parents showed open contempt. Noting the therapist's advocacy for this young boy, I offered a reflective prompt to him: "What feeling comes up for you when you consider Dylan going home each night with parents who act like they don't like him?" The therapist—as he opened his mouth to respond—began to cry. Eyes bleary with tears, he looked at me and said, "That was weird—how did you do that?"

Of course, it wasn't my cunning. I had merely given him a moment of pause and invited his self-reflection. And what he found—what in my experience therapists often find—was sadness. Sadness that is inside him—in inchoate form—because he hadn't noticed nor experienced it, and therefore hadn't metabolized it.

Because most of us are unaccustomed to noticing our continuous feeling state, increasing our awareness may require a deliberate strategy. A good way to initiate this change is to identify a cue that will prompt you to take a quick reflective moment. You might put a Post-it Note somewhere that you will see as a signal to take a quick pause and "make a visit to yourself". The strategy that was most effective for me was to pair this new habit with a routine that I had already established. Before I began any documentation in a client record, I would take a few moments to notice what I was feeling. As I began shaping this new habit, I realized how very unaware of my internal state I had become until I made a pointed effort to cue in to my feelings.

Once you have established a cue for a moment of noticing, you may find that you don't immediately know *what* you are feeling. Because of a lifetime of armoring up against unwelcome feelings we don't have an intrinsic awareness of—or even a vocabulary for—what we are feeling. That's okay—the fact that you have taken a moment to reflect and ask yourself that question is a fine first step.

The next step to knowing what you are feeling is to become aware of what is happening in your body. Just notice how your body is arranging itself. Are you on the edge of your seat? Is your body loose, or is it tightly arranged around protecting your core? Are you experiencing tension anywhere—your neck? Notice especially your jaw and shoulders—that is a place we often hold our tension. Notice your chest—does it feel tight or relaxed? Is your heart beating slow and gently, or is there some racing? Of course, mindfulness practice often includes awareness of the breath, and that is a good place to focus your attention as well. Is your breathing fast and shallow, or deep and rhythmic?

Eventually, our goal is to have a granular understanding of our feeling state. But that level of awareness will take some time to acquire. When I work with clients who have difficulty noticing what they are feeling (e.g., "I don't know, just kinda weird..."), I begin with having them sort their feelings into some gross categories. "Are you mad, sad, glad, or scared?" They could always answer that question. This is a good place for us to begin as well as we begin to develop an increased capacity for noticing our feelings. Am I mad, sad, glad, or scared? Am I relaxed or tense?

Step 4: Allowing

Once we have noticed and identified a feeling, our next action is to simply allow it. Our goal—once again—is to allow a natural and instinctual process to complete itself without interruption. If your current strategy is to pull away when the feeling becomes uncomfortable, this action will be opposite of your impulse. You are practicing how to notice a feeling without reactivity to that feeling.

Allowing feelings is a matter of applying time-honored mindfulness techniques. Your goal is singular: to be totally mindful of this feeling—whether pleasant or unpleasant—and nothing else. As Buddhists say, "Don't push the river". You aren't trying to change anything. Let this river of feeling flow, and watch it with curiosity. It will flow past you of its own accord; you don't have to do anything.

When I teach this "allowing" skill to clients or supervisees, I employ the mindfulness metaphor of standing before a fire. "Your job", I coach, "is to merely watch the fire with heightened awareness. Notice the flame with attention you haven't normally paid. Notice what the flames look like as they lap and rise from the firewood. Notice the heat from the fire—it may feel hot, but it will not burn you. Where you are standing it is safe, so just notice how it feels. You don't need to put this fire out—it will burn itself out as long as you don't put more fuel on it. And you won't add more fuel as long as you are just observing. You don't have to get away from this fire—hold still and observe it. It may get warm—even uncomfortably warm—but it will not harm you. And above all, your job is not to fall into the fire—to become the fire. You are separate from this flame; your only job is to observe it as it grows until it fades".

The application of the observing-the-fire analogy to allowing our feelings is direct. As I notice my feeling, I am already halfway toward my goal because I took time and care to notice it as a feeling state. Now I will stay out of the way of this metabolic process by employing a mindful approach. As soon as I reflect upon what I am feeling, I am no longer "falling into the fire"—the very act of noticing requires a separation between me-being-aware-of-the-feeling and the feeling itself. This dis-identification with the feeling is critical—and it has its own benefit: as I move into reflective mode to observe my feeling, I am moving into a positive task that will help calm me as I disentangle my emotional arousal from myself. This means I won't be adding more fuel to the fire I am observing.

At first, I notice that I am "upset". I reflect on what "upset" is, exactly, and I conclude it is closest to anger (mad, sad, glad, scared, or happy)—I am mad. As I notice what my body is doing, and reflect upon what this feels like, I am "watching the flames". I'm not going to try to dampen down this feeling or distract myself from it—that would be trying to get away from the fire or to put it out. The way to finish the feelings is to experience the feelings. In order to stop feeling sad, we must learn to feel sad.

I remind myself to really notice my anger in a way that I don't normally. As I acknowledge that yes, I am angry, I realize it is because I felt frustrated by my client's failure to follow-through on agreements I had with her. My initial feeling of anger transforms into frustration as I watch it—I am observing the flames with a whole new level of acuity. And—as I observe my frustration, it begins to fade. As I dis-identify from my feelings and my attention focused upon allowing—but not interfering—those feelings begin to fade. I feel much calmer. I can begin to reflect about what my client did or said before my feelings arose. I become curious about my own reaction, and her motivations for doing, or not doing, the things we had agreed to. I have moved from a reactive state to a receptive state. My feelings arose, became more intense, then faded. This is the natural life history of a feeling. We don't have to push this river.

Primary feelings—even when those emotions are intense—will not harm you. But a caveat needs to be made here in the case of people who may have particular sensitivities. Perhaps you have a personal history of trauma. Perhaps you have—due to an especially sensitive nature—an accumulated lifetime of dampening down or distancing from intense emotions. Intense emotions may feel like they will overwhelm you or initiate a cascade of old emotions and images that will overcome you. And when that kind of overwhelm occurs, secondary trauma may occur. The risk, then, is not direct experience of a primary emotion, but there is risk in experiencing secondary feelings of being overwhelmed or helpless. These secondary emotions are laden with cognitive processes and conditioned responses.

Emotional engagement is opening to—and thus desensitizing to—aversive experiences and emotions. But in order for desensitization to be effective, the exposure must be titrated in a way that it doesn't overwhelm the client (or in this case, us). In short, the exposure should result in a successful experience when facing a situation that we previously avoided.

Success doesn't mean pleasurable, but tolerable. Opening to intense unpleasant situations must be initiated in a way that you feel that you are choosing the level of exposure and that you can "step away" from the feelings if they threaten to overwhelm you.

Perhaps for you, in some situations, it may be necessary to dip into the feeling and then to step back. Even if the stepping back consists of distraction or some other form of avoidance, that is a fine place to begin. We are developing a muscle, and we can't expect ourselves to be fully proficient right away. This is a dance between safety and risk. The goal is to accept a little bit more of the feeling than we did previously. Even one second more counts. Think of this as a kind of emotion yoga—you are both respecting your personal limits and pushing up to those limits to expand them.

You may believe that you need to avoid certain situations because they are emotionally "triggering". But a caveat here is that our ability to avoid triggers is limited when we do trauma work because so much of the work is potentially provocative. And—if we identify too many triggers in the work—we are on the very path of experiential avoidance that we are working to change. We must respect our personal limits, but the goal of this experiential engagement domain is to de-potentiate triggers rather than to simply declare them and leave them unattended.

We must also accept that we may not be able to do this as we begin to open the "soft front". If the feeling/situation is especially provocative, you may have to begin via mental imagery—mentally approaching the feelings or situation. You can change the scene when you reach your personal limit. Practice via imagery before the real, *in vivo* experience. The important thing is to realize you are choosing to feel the sensation, and at any time, you can step away. You aren't helpless, and you won't be overwhelmed. And—perhaps this goes without saying—if you experience triggers of your own unresolved trauma history, you will need the support of your own professional helper.

Full experiential engagement is, at the same time, easy to conceptualize and very difficult to do. This skill will require a career to fully master. Jim Valvano, the former basketball coach of North Carolina State, gave a legendary speech in acceptance of an ESPY award. He gave this speech as he was suffering from a terminal illness. Valvano advised that there were three things we should do every day. "If you laugh, you think, and you cry, that's a full day". Valvano said, "That's a heck of a day. You do that seven days a week, you're going to have something special". If you learn how to laugh, think, and cry every day in your work as a trauma therapist then you are going to have a very special career.

Experiential Engagement

You Must Remember This

- The chemical events we call "feelings" must be experienced fully in order to be metabolized. We can't selectively experience some and not others.
- If we try to tamp down negative feelings, we also numb ourselves to positive feelings. There is a direct link between trying to avoid negative feelings/experiences and reduced pleasure and reward from the work.
- When we try to escape negative feelings, we also seek to avoid the situations that cause those feelings. As we do that, we begin to disengage from the full experience of our work. This disengagement is the first step toward burnout. Our anxiety about dreaded tasks grows, and the pleasure we experience from our work diminishes.
- Experiential engagement can be described as "avoiding avoidance", that is, opening up to and fully experiencing those things we have been avoiding. Counterintuitively, the way to enhance our sense of well-being on the job and experience the rewards of doing intense trauma work is to open ourselves to the difficult and uncomfortable aspects of the work and to experience difficult feelings through to the end of that metabolic event.

Bridging Concepts to Skills

- Our ability to engage intensity is developed by:

    - **Setting an intention:** See the target you are aiming for. "I am open and willing to experience uncomfortable emotions—and the situations that evoke them; I will enhance my ability to notice and acknowledge those feelings, and I will improve my ability to allow difficult feelings to run their course without stopping them".
    - **Enhancing willingness:** Explicitly answer the question: what am I going to do with the pain/discomfort that arises from doing trauma work? Answering in writing is even better. The possible answers are really only two: 1) I will try to avoid it/numb myself to it, or 2) I will open to it, knowing it will be hard and painful.
    - **Noticing:** Define how and when you will remind yourself to check-in to reflect on your feelings. Begin by attending to any physical sensations (e.g., chest tightness, heart rate, breathing, headache, muscle tightness).
    - **Allowing:** When you identify your feeling state, imagine your feelings to be a fire that you are standing before. Notice your feelings with curiosity and focused attention without feeding the flames (reacting to your feelings), without trying to pull back from the fire (distracting from or turning down your feelings), and without trying to put the fire out (denying your feelings to yourself or others). The goal is to maintain a simple, non-reactive

interest in your feelings. Watch them arise, strengthen, and fade. You don't have to do anything to change them.

Entering the Woods at the Darkest Place

Self-Audit

1. Which best describes your natural tendency when confronted with a situation that causes you anxiety?

    a. I want to try to forget it—pull the blanket over my head, or grab the TV remote control and tell everyone I'm stressed and can't be bothered;

    b. I want to talk the situation through with a friend or significant other;

    c. I want to take an action that deals in some way with the situation.

2. J'accuse! Would you plead guilty or innocent if I accused you of tending to avoid the following over your career?

    a. Angry, non-compliant clients;
    b. Highly narcissistic clients;
    c. Clients with borderline personality;
    d. Clients with profound grief issues;
    e. Unengaged, difficult to motivate clients.

3. Consider what feelings you might tend to avoid. Here are some feelings that are difficult for everyone to experience. For you, which are the hardest? As an exercise to develop a more detailed self-examination of your profile, rank these feeling states according to the ones you are *most willing to experience* to the ones you *tend to avoid.* (1 = most willing; 8 = least willing to experience):

Frustration	Rank: _____
Helplessness	Rank: _____
Boredom	Rank: _____
Fear/Anxiety	Rank: _____
Embarrassment	Rank: _____
Anger	Rank: _____
Grief	Rank: _____
Sadness	Rank: _____

4. As you survey your own engagement vs. avoidant tendencies over your career, can you identify a situation that you once avoided that you learned to open up to? How—and why—did you become willing to engage it? Did it require learning a new skill, or just a new spirit of willingness?

5. Reflect on your responses to this self-audit, and what you know about yourself. Using the descriptive statements as a guide, draw the

needle on the experiential engagement gauge (scale = 1–10) where
you would currently rate yourself:

Descriptive Statements:

Gray (1-4)	I am open and willing to experience discomfort, anxiety, sadness, and other aversive emotions—and the situations that evoke them— and to acknowledge my feelings to allow them to run their course.
Light Gray (5-7)	I am sometimes willing to open to discomfort, but I maintain a tendency to avoid certain feelings or situations that I cannot tolerate.
Black (8-10)	I often avoid feelings or situations that cause me stress.

References

Blake, W. (1804). *Eternity.* Retrieved from https://poets.org/poem/eternity.

Brach, T. (2003). *Radical acceptance: Embracing your life with the heart of a Buddha.* New York: Bantam Books.

Brimhall, T. (2018, January 29). *Dear eros.* The New Yorker.

Cain, Susan. (2012) *Quiet: The power of introverts in a world that can't stop talking.* New York: Crown Publishers.

Donaldson-Feilder, E. J., & Bond, F. W. (2004). The relative importance of psychological acceptance and emotional intelligence to workplace well-being. *British Journal of Guidance and Counselling, 32*(2), 187–203.

Fish, Matthew T. (2014). *Casual video game play as an augmentation intervention for anxiety: A controlled study* (Doctoral dissertation, East Carolina University).

Gregg, J. A. (2004). *A randomized controlled effectiveness trial comparing patient education with and without acceptance and commitment therapy for type 2 diabetes self-management* (Doctoral dissertation, University of Nevada, Reno).

Grob, J. (2009). *Dial E for emotion: Context and consequences of emotion regulation* (Doctoral dissertation, University of Groningen).

Hayes, S. C., Bissett, R. T., Korn, Z., Zettle, R. D., Rosenfarb, I. S., Cooper, L. D., & Grundt, A. M. (1999). The impact of acceptance versus control rationales on pain tolerance. *The Psychological Record, 49*(1), 33–47.

Hayes, S. C., Strosahl, K., Wilson, K. G., Bissett, R. T., Pistorello, J., Toarmino, D., & Stewart, S. H. (2004). Measuring experiential avoidance: A preliminary test of a working model. *The Psychological Record, 54*(4), 553–578.

Iglesias, M. E. L., de Bengoa Vallejo, R. B., & Fuentes, P. S. (2010). The relationship between experiential avoidance and burnout syndrome in critical care nurses: A cross-sectional questionnaire survey. *International Journal of Nursing Studies, 47*(1), 30–37.

Karekla, M., Forsyth, J. P., & Kelly, M. M. (2004). Emotional avoidance and panicogenic responding to a biological challenge procedure. *Behavior Therapy, 35*(4), 725–746.

Kashdan, T. B., Barrios, V., Forsyth, J. P., & Steger, M. F. (2006). Experiential avoidance as a generalized psychological vulnerability: Comparisons with coping and emotion regulation strategies. *Behaviour Research and Therapy, 44*(9), 1301–1320.

Keen, Sam. (1991). *Fire in the belly.* New York: Bantam Books.

Kroska, E. B., Calarge, C., O'Hara, M. W., Deumic, E., & Dindo, L. (2017). Burnout and depression in medical students: Relations with avoidance and disengagement. *Journal of Contextual Behavioral Science, 6*(4), 404–408.

Levy, A. (2020, January 13). *The New Yorker, newyorker.com.*

Marchica, L. A., Mills, D. J., Keough, M. T., & Derevensky, J. L. (2020). Exploring differences among video gamers with and without depression: Contrasting emotion regulation and mindfulness. *Cyberpsychology, Behavior, and Social Networking, 23*(2), 119–125.

Marx, B. P., & Sloan, D. M. (2005). Peritraumatic dissociation and experiential avoidance as predictors of posttraumatic stress symptomatology. *Behaviour Research and Therapy, 43*(5), 569–583.

Milani, L., Camisasca, E., Ionio, C., Miragoli, S., & Di Blasio, P. (2019). Video games use in childhood and adolescence: Social phobia and differential susceptibility to media effects. *Clinical Child Psychology and Psychiatry*, 1359104519882754.

Mitchell, S. (1994). *A book of psalms: Selected and adapted from the hebrew*, translated and adapted by Stephen Mitchell. New York: HarperCollins Publishers.

Mohrmann, M. (*personal communication, April 20*, 2020).

Naidoo, L. J., DeCriscio, A., Bily, H., Manipella, A., Ryan, M., & Youdim, J. (2012). The 2 × 2 model of goal orientation and burnout: The role of approach–avoidance dimensions in predicting burnout. *Journal of Applied Social Psychology*, *42*(10), 2541–2563.

Nepo, M. (2011). *The book of awakening: Having the life you want by being present to the life you have.* Berkeley, CA: Conari Press.

Nguyen, T., & Landau, S. (2019). Effects of gaming on children's brains: Depression and social isolation. *Advances in Social Sciences Research Journal*, *6*(9), 291–302.

Nhất Hạnh, T. (1999). *The heart of the Buddha's teaching: Transforming suffering into peace, joy & liberation: The four noble truths, the noble eightfold path, and other basic Buddhist teachings.* New York: Broadway Books.

Polman, R., Borkoles, E., & Nicholls, A. R. (2010). Type D personality, stress, and symptoms of burnout: The influence of avoidance coping and social support. *British Journal of Health Psychology*, *15*(3), 681–696.

Powers, M. B., & Emmelkamp, P. M. (2008). Virtual reality exposure therapy for anxiety disorders: A meta-analysis. *Journal of Anxiety Disorders*, *22*(3), 561–569.

Rilke, R. M. (n.d.). *Letters to a young poet*. Retrieved from http://www.columbia.edu/~ey2172/rilke.html.

Taylor, Jill Bolte. (2008). My stroke of insight: A brain scientist's personal journey. New York: Viking.

Trungpa, C. (2001). *Great Eastern sun: The wisdom of Shambhala*. Boston, MA: Shambhala.

van Dernoot Lipsky, L. D., & Burk, C. (2009). *Trauma stewardship: An everyday guide to caring for self while caring for others.* Oakland, CA: Berrett-Koehler.

Vilardaga, R., Luoma, J. B., Hayes, S. C., Pistorello, J., Levin, M. E., Hildebrandt, M. J., & Bond, F. (2011). Burnout among the addiction counseling workforce: The differential roles of mindfulness and values-based processes and work-site factors. *Journal of Substance Abuse Treatment*, *40*(4), 323–335.

Von Der Heiden, J. M., Braun, B., Müller, K. W., & Egloff, B. (2019). The association between video gaming and psychological functioning. *Frontiers in Psychology*, *10*, 1731.

3 Reducing Rumination: Getting Free from the Ghosts That Follow

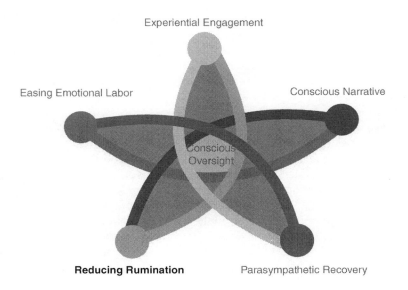

Experiential Engagement

Easing Emotional Labor

Conscious Narrative

Conscious Oversight

Reducing Rumination

Parasympathetic Recovery

> My life has been filled with terrible misfortunes. Most of which never happened.
>
> Michel de Montaigne

> Just leave it lay where Jesus flung it.
>
> Overheard at farmer's market

You have a picture of your "happy place". Maybe it is a landscape photo of a beautiful place that you visited on a cherished vacation. Or maybe it is a picture of your child when they were at that moment-of-perfect-cuteness at age four (before they grew up and discovered social media and would only talk to you in one-word replies). Maybe you're using one of those happy place pictures as a screen saver on your laptop. And—when your laptop isn't in active use—that picture inserts itself onto the computer screen. A reminder of your happy place. If you take a moment to pay attention, the picture may rekindle a moment of happy reflection.

I've got good news and bad news. The good news is that your brain also has a screen saver function. In moments in which you are not focused on some activity and you let your mind wander, your brain's "screen saver" comes on without any effort on your part. And it may surprise you to learn that each day, your brain is in screen-saver mode about half of the time you are awake. Your brain's screen is filled with these automatic, self-generated images about the same amount of time that your brain is paying attention to what you are doing (Killingsworth & Gilbert, 2010).

The bad news? Much of the time—depending on how much stress you have experienced and your own unique tendency, your brain's screen saver isn't always producing pictures of your happy place. It is replaying that stressful trauma case that you dealt with today. It is running images of the conflict you had with a co-worker. It is conjuring images of the abuse your child client experienced. The more that screen saver runs the images of that trauma case, the more intense your negative feelings will be. And, completing the bad news, the more negative your emotional state is, in circular fashion, the more active this negative "screen-saver" function becomes (Deng et al., 2014; Smallwood et al., 2009).

In more familiar terms, I am talking about rumination. This screen saver in our brain is—much of the time—replaying negative and stressful experiences. In the previous chapter, I encouraged you to enter the woods at the darkest place, to fully engage difficult emotions and situations. Your willingness to engage difficult material allows a full expression of the emotion, and a full metabolization of the chemical event that is that emotion. We are allowing it to be over and done. These experiences don't last very long, and neither do our primary feelings. But—because of the brain's tendency toward this screen-saver function—we can watch a replay of those brief experiences throughout the day, and sometimes even longer. Your limbic system will respond to the replay just as if you are in that experience right now, recreating the stress. That is why, in order to complete the metabolization of these difficult emotions, we might need a strategy to compliment the engagement skills I have described in Chapter 2.

Robert Sopolski, in his cleverly titled book *Why Zebras Don't Get Ulcers*, makes a salient point about the recycling of stressful events that our human brain does: "For the vast majority of beasts on this planet, stress is about a short-term crisis, after which it's either over with or you're over with" (2004). For the zebra, this is about two minutes of screaming terror on the savanna as the lioness pursues, after which the danger is over. Or the zebra is over.

We humans are not normal mammals in this regard. These two minutes of terror are the brief chemical events—emotions—that neuroscientists describe. They are quickly over and done. But we abnormal mammals are proud possessors of an especially advanced cerebral cortex. That means we have conscious awareness, unlike the zebra. For the zebra, fear originates in the visual center and moves upward from the occipital to parietal part of the brain. The zebra experiences fear—life and death terror—*but not worry*. Zebras are either afraid in the face of an imminent danger or they are calmly munching grass on the savanna. We, on the other hand, possess the rare talent of self-generated thought: images. We can conjure images in the higher parts of our brain that move downward from the parietal to the occipital and then to the limbic system, where emotions are produced. We have a special talent—we can experience not only fear and terror like the zebra, but also worry and anxiety. The 90-second event that Jill Bolt Taylor described—or the two minutes of screaming terror that Robert Sapolsky describes—can be recreated for the rest of the day. Or week. Or career.

Feelings, as I discussed in Chapter 2, are brief chemical events. But what I am now describing is not a primary emotion event. I am describing a *cognitive* event. You may recall the old Doritos tagline "Go ahead—eat all you want; we'll make more". Ruminations are your brain saying, "Go ahead—feel all you want; I'll make more". This creation of thoughts and images is the process whereby a brief stressful event can cause stress not just during the experience, but all day long or longer. Ninety seconds just became two hours—or more. This is also the process by which anxiety is produced, our mood is changed, our ability to sleep is diminished. This cognitive recycling is an elemental component of secondary traumatic stress.

Forgive me for the hackneyed approach but I wish to introduce rumination with the Merriam-Webster dictionary definition. But in this case, I want you to take note of both aspects of the Merriam-Webster medical definition of "rumination" (n.d.):

a. *the act or process of regurgitating and chewing again previously swallowed food*
b. *obsessive thinking about an idea, situation, or choice especially when it interferes with normal mental functioning specifically: a focusing of one's attention on negative or distressing thoughts or feelings that when excessive or prolonged may lead to or exacerbate an episode of depression*

When I describe rumination as an elemental component of secondary traumatic stress, I am referring to the thoughts that we have repetitively that rekindle feelings of stress from an earlier experience. Rumination is "chewing again previously swallowed food" (thoughts). In the medical definition, note the specification that rumination refers to "the focusing of one's attention on negative or distressing thoughts or feelings that when excessive or prolonged may lead to or exacerbate an episode of depression". For our purposes, I will extend that definition beyond the clinical case of depression to the more daily "may lead to or exacerbate a negative experience".

Simply put, in my operational definition, *rumination is a continuation of stressful events through mental re-imagining that is distressing rather than problem solving.* Rumination is "stress-stretching", extending the stress reaction beyond the actual event. And since rumination is a cognitive event, our control of this stress-inducing phenomenon must also refer to *cognitive* skills.

Sapolsky (2004, p. 15–16) has a pithy way of summarizing the helpful and harmful aspects of the stress response into two simple statements: fact #1: "If you get stressed dealing with an acute physical challenge, and you cannot appropriately *turn on* the stress-response, you're in big trouble"; and fact #2: "...if you cannot *turn off* the stress-response at the end of a stress event, the stress-response can become damaging". We need to able to turn on the stress response—also known as fight or flight—and we need to be able to turn it off—rest and recovery.

Turning the stress response on and off is precisely the cognitive breath: inhalation and exhalation. "Inhaling" is another way of describing the act of opening to experiential engagement. When we open to engagement, we are allowing our stress response to activate. Now—as I move to the skills for reducing rumination, I am beginning to describe the exhale, turning the stress response off. Learning how to consciously manage our ruminations—to let the event be over when the experience is over—is how we cognitively "exhale".

The CE-CERT skills are—as I have described—transactional. Consider how much easier it is for you to willingly engage an intense experience if you have confidence that you can turn the stress response off after you have turned it on. And, working the other direction, it is easier to turn the stress response off if you have opened up fully to the experience and allowed its initial energy to be metabolized, to be fully expended.

I will use a case example: You are a trauma therapist caring for a child with a profound trauma history. This case is especially provocative for you—perhaps the abuse is especially egregious, or perhaps you have a special amount of empathy and identification for this child. You open a "soft front" to this child and this trauma. You experience strong feelings of sadness and empathy for what that child experienced. You experience a strong impulse to advocate for and care for this child. You feel pressure about making sure you do everything you can for her. For the whole 90-minute initial session with your client and her new caregiver, you are engaged and feeling intently. You take a few moments afterwards to reflect on how you are experiencing this case (good for you!). You can identify what you are feeling: sadness about her pain, pressure to handle this case effectively, affection for a child who deserved better.

Now let's advance to one hour after your experience with this little girl and her caregiver. You have seen another client by now and are beginning to do some routine documentation tasks. Your mind begins to return to this little girl and all that she has been through. You begin to have images of the abuse that she experienced. You begin to replay things that her caseworker said that you thought were invalidating to this little girl's experience. The longer you experience these thoughts and feelings, the more upset you feel—sad for this girl, and angry at the caseworker.

The feelings that you are experiencing one hour after your clinical session is not experiential engagement. You are not experiencing the event; you are re-experiencing your mental reconstruction of the event. And that—by the way—means that you are not experiencing whatever is happening right now before you. Experience-sampling research has established that the longer you spend reviewing past experiences such as this, the higher your anxiety and the lower your mood (Ruby et al., 2013). This mental re-hashing is an important element in secondary trauma.

We don't want to spend a long time doing these sorts of mental reviews. The problem is not that you followed my advice—and the evidence—and opened up to the experience in the first place. The initial experience is over. You did a great job of opening to it and taking a moment to pause and note your feelings. The wave of feeling arose, strengthened, and faded. Now it is time to turn the activation of the stress response off and to open to what is before you now. Now is the time to rest your mind from that case.

As I introduce the concept of resting the mind, it brings us to a critical point in our discussion of secondary trauma/job stress. Secondary trauma is not produced merely by exposure to a stress event; it is that we don't know how to turn the stress response off. The problem is not that a stressful event *activated* fight or flight, but rather that we never *stop* "fighting or fleeing".

You might find it surprising that you have intrusive thoughts just as often as do people with obsessive-compulsive disorder. Ninety-four percent of us have been distressed by intrusive thoughts in the last three months (Radomsky et al., 2014). We are talking to ourselves in our heads constantly. This self-talk may be random, neutral thoughts or worries ("Did I lock the front door?"), but after an emotionally evocative experience, our intrusive thoughts are very likely to be an emotional review of that stressor. These imaginal "stress reviews" become the screen saver in our brain anytime we aren't actively engaged in something compelling enough to activate the task centers of the brain. In short, we keep replaying that stressful event, and that keeps the stress response alive.

What I have been calling your brain's screen saver has been identified by brain researchers as the default mode network (DMN). This network has been recognized and studied only relatively recently. The DMN is the network of brain structures that are active when we are not focused outwardly on a task—just like the screen saver on your computer. It is worth noting that the DMN has been described as "survival salient" (Buckner et al., 2008), meaning that our brain is working toward keeping us alive and well. The purpose of this mental review is to consider past dangers and project us forward into potential actions. In short, we are moving back and forth from the past (worry and re-traumatization) to the future (preparing for what I must do tomorrow). And this time travel can be exhausting when it becomes repetitive and we can't turn it off.

In order to be healthy, as Sapolsky noted, we need to be able to activate the fight-or-flight mechanism when we are before a threat. But—and here is where rumination comes in—we don't only turn on the fight-or-flight system when we are in an emergency. We also turn it on when we *think* we are in an emergency, or when we *imagine* a past emergency, or we *anticipate* an emergency—even though at the time we are completely safe.

In order to not be in a constant state of emergency—a perpetual state of stress—you need to rest your mind after those encounters. We need to find the borders of these stressors so that they have a beginning and an end. But how do we do that?

Everyone knows that when you are physically tired you rest by merely holding still. You're tired because you just took a long run? Lie down on the couch with a cool drink and hold still. Get a good night's sleep. Hold still, and your body recovers. But consider what happens when your try to rest your mind by holding it still—it becomes *more* active. Indeed, one of the ways the DMN was discovered was researchers began noting the pattern of increased brain activity in some areas of brains of subjects who were lying in imaging machines but hadn't yet received instructions to do or think about something. They were inactive, but their brains revealed increased activity.

One of the first terms ascribed to the DMN was the "task negative network". The term "task negative" evokes a puzzle: how can we rest when doing so is "task negative", but resting increases ruminations that make us tired? Entertaining the "task negative" concept as a puzzle also suggests the beginning of a solution: what activities are "task positive" but at the same time mentally restful?

Matthew Killingsworth and Daniel Gilbert (2010) conducted famous—and still ongoing—research that sampled people's mental state during various activities in real time. Using a mobile phone app, they collected experience-sampling data from over 2,000 people (now over 35,000 people). At random intervals, the participants would be asked questions about how they were *feeling* at that precise moment, what they are *doing*, and whether they were thinking about what they were doing or thinking about something else. The results of this study—as they were initially reported in 2010—is apparent in the title of their *Science* journal report: "The Wandering Mind is an Unhappy Mind".

The results of this research are both fascinating and relevant for our search for ways to rest the mind. What activities are people engaged in that corresponded with the best mood state? According to Killingsworth, we are happiest when we are (in descending order): 1) making love; 2) exercising; and 3) in conversation. We are *unhappiest* when we are—of all the activities they categorized—resting! The very thing that we do in order to rest the mind—holding still—is absolutely the least restful thing to do.

There is much we can mine from the Killingsworth and Gilbert study. Look again at the three activities people are doing when they are happiest. They are very different types of activities. In fact, there is only one thing that they have in common: they are highly *absorbing* activities. Absorbing, in the sense that they hold the focus of the mind on the activity you are doing (making love, exercising, conversing) and do not allow the mind to wander.

Now consider the activities in which we are engaged (disengaged from?) when we are the unhappiest. We are unhappiest when we are resting. That is a stunning finding. The very thing that you may yearn for when you are the most stressed is the most unhappiness-inducing state to be in. When you come home after a particularly stressful day at work, what do you do? Do you tell everyone you had a stressful day, grab the remote control, and order takeout? We tell ourselves that what we need is some downtime. It seems that resting is all we have the capacity for. But it isn't true. And it isn't effective at improving our mood or resting our mind. You will return to work the next day a little more depleted, and a little less motivated, even though you spent last night "resting".

And—before I am done mining the Killingsworth data—there is a point that must be made about the penultimate most-unhappiness-inducing activity on their list: working. Because I will be discussing how to reduce emotional labor at work in Chapter 5, I want to make a nuanced point about work and our experience of happiness. Killingsworth's data suggested that we are unhappier at work than during any other activity except resting. But LeFevre's (1988) earlier research suggests that we are three times more likely to be in a flow state when we are at work than when we are on vacation.

I don't find these two studies to be in contradiction. Killingworth's experience samples revealed—true enough—that we are often unhappy when we are at work. But it also reveals that we are mind-wandering about half of the time we are at work. Their data ultimately concluded that *where* we are has less to do with our mood state than *whether our attention* is focused on what we are doing or if we are mind-wandering. Furthermore, third on the list of unhappiness-inducing activities involve being on the computer—which is, of course, often exactly what we are doing when we are at work. Apparently, being on the computer often isn't very engaging.

In the final analysis, then, it isn't really being at work that makes us unhappy. Being *at work while being disengaged from our work activities* makes us unhappy. Being at work while we are highly engaged creates a sense of flow, as LeFevre established. And flow is a highly enjoyable state. And—foreshadowing what is to come in this chapter—engagement is a restful and renewing place to be. Engagement is the opposite of rumination.

Concepts to Skills: How Do We Rest the Mind?

Set the Target

Developing our skills in reducing ruminations begins by setting an intention—seeing the target. Try to picture your goal in specific terms. I will suggest the goal here: you want—after fully opening up to an intense stressful experience (that may include trauma exposure)—to leave that moment in *that* moment, and not to carry the negative emotions into *this* moment. You want it to be done. You want your body to recover, which means that you turn off the stress response and let your physiological processes return to homeostasis. You want your mind also to recover, to be capable of rest. You want to develop the ability to deactivate the DMN when it is producing ruminative thoughts and images.

We all have wandering minds—our brain has evolved to go to screen-saver mode throughout the day—and that's a feature, not a bug. But we want to become skillful at recognizing when we are ruminating in a nonproductive way that extends the stress and lowers our mood and problem-solving ability. When we recognize that we are ruminating, we want to skillfully free ourselves from the "ghosts that have followed us home".

If you haven't already, you may need to start here: give yourself permission to let your ruminations go. Some therapists have an unarticulated belief that their caring is genuine only if they are suffering for their client. I was in clinical supervision with a child therapist who was caring for a four-year-old boy who had suffered the trauma of child abuse. As I began coaching this very passionate therapist about giving her mind some rest—some recovery time—her response brought me up short. She said this to me, "How dare I, Brian? How dare I just let this go because it's evening and I'm at home? How dare I go home and have a lovely evening with my son and husband knowing what this little boy went through? You need to understand this about me: this isn't just a job; I genuinely care about him".

I hope I didn't betray it in my reply to her, but frankly I was gobsmacked. This is superstitious thinking—it is superstition to believe that your suffering, your sacrifice of your enjoyment of the evening in some way helps your client. It does not. And I've learned that she isn't an anomaly, many therapists have similar thinking—they believe that genuine care is represented by suffering enough for the client in "real life", and not "just the job". Not only does your intentional suffering not help your clients, contraiwise, but it will render you less caring in the long run.

The ability to care and the ability to not care are not in contradiction. These two concepts are twin dynamics of the same caring action. In order to care, we must be able to let that emotion run its natural metabolic course—just like any of the negative emotions. If I interrupt this process by not allowing the sense of caring to fade—clinging to my sense of caring—I will gradually lose my ability to care at all. It is important to have my sense of caring available to me for this client that is before me right now, and I can't do that if I'm still clinging to the caring of the client I saw yesterday. I will tire. I will burn out. I will lose the ability to care.

It is unsurprising to learn that the so-called "super-meditators"—those Zen monks who have meditated for more than 10,000 hours—experience compassion more frequently than do average people. What is surprising, perhaps, is that the episodes of compassion experienced by these monks are briefer than the average person's experience of compassion (Lutz et al., 2008). They are better at caring than are we "mere mortals". But they are also better at not caring.

Notice and Acknowledge Ruminations

Now you have the vision of developing a "non-sticky" brain that will allow intense experience to move through without endless re-creation of the stress event. The first practice is to increase recognition when a thought begins to recycle unproductively. You need to practice re-cognizing rumination and that it is, in fact, a rumination. You shouldn't be afraid of the default-mode network. Enjoy your daydreams; you will get some of your best ideas there. But after a stress event, these self-generated thoughts are much more likely to be re-creating the negative experience. In these cases, your goal is to quickly notice that you are ruminating, and to label it as that.

Maybe you have a different term that describes rumination—brooding, mental spinning, worrying, pondering. Identifying the difference between rumination and problem solving is harder than it may sound. We do a lot of mind-wandering. Sometimes this mind-wandering is creative thinking. Sometimes, in fact, we solve problems in this mode. When they are po-sitive or productive—especially when they include future events—these images may even improve your mood and energy. The default mode is where we define our sense of self. That is a good thing.

But sometimes, we are lost in reimagining situations that caused us stress. We are doing nothing but passively re-experiencing the stress or even trauma of that experience. Our fight-or-flight system is activated each time we imagine that scene, "She had no right to say that to me...!" but there is no resolution to the fight or flight. Our brain creates the image, our limbic system fires, we become more emotionally dysregulated, which increases the image-making of our brain, and we are now caught in a loop between the images that increase emotional arousal and emotional arousal that increases mental imaging. That endless loop between those two mechanisms defines rumination.

Although ruminations can be very unpleasant, this recycling can be quite seductive. We may have the sense that we are trying to "work it through" in our mind. And, in fact, sometimes we are working it out. But sometimes we are simply caught in this endless mental looping. Caught in the Escher painting, we are the monks climbing the endless set of stairs that are always going up but illogically lead only back to the exact spot where they began. Indeed, research on the default mode shows that the longer we spend ruminating, the *poorer* our problem-solving ability is. We have a sense that we are working something out, but we are just wearing ourselves out. And our stress response remains stuck in the "on" position.

Once you step out of the imagery and ask yourself, "Am I problem solving or am I ruminating?", the answer may be apparent. This is the query you want to make of these repeating thoughts. Pay attention to these two qualities that distinguish problem solving from rumination: 1) Is there an *action* that I need to take about this situation, or am I just passively re-watching this scene? 2) Is my anxiety and mood *improving or worsening* as I engage in this mental review?

When you notice that you are ruminating, acknowledge it and label it. Just as with feeling identification, labeling the rumination (spinning, brooding, whatever you call it) helps you to dis-identify with the rumination. This may sound something like this: "I am just spinning; this is just making me more anxious. I can let this go".

Once you recognize that you are ruminating and establish the goal of stepping out of the rumination cycle, you are more than halfway to that very goal. Instead of being lost in the rumination imagery, you are now focusing on the fact that you are ruminating. That means that, already, you are no longer lost in thought. As you pause to consider how to step out of the rumination, the thinking that you are doing is already task positive.

Problem solving consists of defining an action that you can take. Contrast that with rumination, in which you are passively buffeted by the self-perpetuating loop between images and stress. It is this circuit that we need to disrupt in order to allow the rumination to quiet itself. And when we go into active problem solving, we are doing exactly that.

Short-Circuit the Cognitive–Emotional Link

Understanding how our limbic system responds to images helps us understand the energy dynamic of ruminations. The cerebral cortex (that produces these images) has neural connectivity with the limbic system, which produces emotions. This is a two-way highway. When I conjure the image of the difficult session that I had this morning with a trauma client, these images activate the amygdala and I experience a stress reaction (fight-or-flight response). Because my limbic system is now on alert, the mental imaging intensifies (looking for dangers in the environment.) This, in turn, energizes the stress response. We now have an energy loop between cognition and emotions, each fueling the other. This loop can self-perpetuate for hours or even days. This loop is exactly why we don't experience stress as a 90-second chemical event, but rather, as a continuous environmental circumstance.

The primary stress exposure is the reason we turned the stress switch on. High-demand situations require that—we need to go into stress mode to remain healthy. But we should understand that our stress after exposure is not from the original event but is coming from a recycling neural circuit. In people without a clinical disorder, this circuit (the circuit from image-conjuring to stress-response) can be de-energized if the circuit is interrupted for as little as two minutes. We just need a strategy for getting out of the looping for a few minutes. This fact is our opportunity to allow the stressful event to come to its natural end.

In the rumination disorder treatment literature, interruption of the cycle is termed "distraction". But terming the strategy distraction places the emphasis back on the stressful event we are distracting from—"I am distracting from what happened today". We want to resist the siren song of the default mode which will pull us back into the cognitive imaging–emotional response cycle of thinking about that stressful event. It isn't *not* thinking about something; it is, rather, thinking about something more immediate than the stress event. It is about putting our attention on something in the here-and-now rather than in the there-and-then.

In other words, it isn't *distraction*, but rather, *absorption* that de-energizes the rumination. Being distracted isn't task positive, but being absorbed in an activity that holds our attention away from self-referential thoughts is exactly the definition of task positive.

When I recognize that I am ruminating and need to break that cycle, I therefore want to direct myself towards an absorbing activity. It is unfortunate that we refer to this as the "task positive network". It needn't be a "task", and in fact, may be much more absorbing if it doesn't feel like a task. Perhaps you can think of your "go-to" activity that you find absorbing. Wood working? Knitting? The only criterion is that the activity must be wholly absorbing. Any activity that allows your attention to be shared between the rumination and the activity will fail to break the ruminative cycle.

Rumination can be a vortex that pulls you back time and time again into the rumination mode. If you have had a particularly stressful day you are likely to feel exhausted as you walk through the front door of your home. This exhaustion results from the energy costs of keeping your emotions in check. You tamped down your stress response so that you could professionally accomplish the things you needed to. But now you are home. Now, you will say, "I just want to crash and do nothing". The fact that children, partners, meal preparation, and other life demands don't allow us to do this may add to the stress. But our impulse is—to the extent we are able—to do nothing. We just wish to rest, to emotionally recover. We want as little stimulation as possible. Just sit and watch something mindlessly soothing on TV.

And here is our mistake. As I've said, we can't rest the mind by holding still. Passively watching TV—or passively doing anything else—allows our mind to move into the vortex of our rumination: survival-salient thinking—reviewing past experiences and conjuring future worries. Reliving the stress that I endured today at work and thinking about the dreaded tasks I have to deal with tomorrow. It's not surprising that I'm tired and that I want to think about anything except work. *But it is a rumination trap if I begin to reduce stimulation.* The more I involve myself in "mindless" activities (more precisely, non-activities), the more I ruminate. And the more I ruminate, the higher my anxiety, the lower my mood, and the worse my problem-solving ability.

You know by now that in order to break the rumination cycle, you must move out of the default mode and into task positive mode. But that doesn't mean that you need to go prepare your annual taxes. "Task positive" doesn't mean that the activity must feel like work. When you are exhausted and stressed out, you don't feel like working. That is why I proposed the concept of an *absorbing* activity. Look again at the top activities that Killingworth and Gilbert's subjects are engaged in when they are not mind-wandering (making love, exercising, conversation). They are all enjoyable activities, not "tasks".

This isn't making yourself do something because it is good for you. We all know that relying on sheer willpower never works for very long. This can't be about making yourself eat your vegetables. It is too hard to make ourselves do something when we are emotionally exhausted.

Select an absorbing activity that engages you—that maintains your attention away from self-referential thoughts. Meditation is often promoted for this purpose. That is because meditation is, in spite of all appearances, a task positive activity. If you practice meditation you know that unlike in cliché, meditation isn't blissing out by "clearing the mind". It is, rather, *focusing* the mind upon the breath or some other singular point-of-focus. That makes meditation not only an option for reducing rumination, but also a fine model of an absorbing activity.

The musician and artist John Cage, speaking to the painter Philip Guston, said, "When you start working, everybody is in your studio—the past, your friends, enemies, the art world, and above all, your own ideas—all are there. But as you continue painting, they start leaving, one by one, and you are left completely alone. Then, if you are lucky, even you leave" (Patterson, 2008).

The "you" that leaves is the DMN—where your concept of "you" is maintained. And like Cage, at the end of that stressful day, everyone is in our "studio": our friends, those we've had conflict with, all of the stressful things that we experienced that day. And then, as we move into an absorbing activity—they leave. And then, as you become absorbed in what you are doing, you leave. You stop thinking about yourself and your own stress, and you begin to focus on what you are doing. And you have broken the vicious and endlessly perpetuating cycle between thought and emotion.

In the quiet reflection of this moment—as you are reading this book—think about what absorbs you in this way. If you practice meditation, that is a good option to keep at the ready. When you exercise, does it absorb you in this way? Is it something that you are easily motivated to do, or is it effortful to get yourself to do it? Remember, after a stressful day when you are ruminating, you may not have the willpower to make yourself do something that feels unpleasant. We are identifying that activity that—for you—absorbs your attention completely.

Television watching deserves special mention since it is the activity many people are drawn to when they are emotionally exhausted. Is watching television an effective distraction from rumination? I already made the point that *passive* television watching isn't enough to hold our minds away from the vortex of the rumination. In general, television watching tends to be passive and may allow our minds to continue to wander in and out of attention to the program. And just like the tongue finding the broken tooth, our mind will return to the rumination over and over—even when it is causing a sore spot.

But if that is true of passive television watching, what about *active* television watching? Is active television watching an oxymoron? This isn't an area that is much researched, but it is worth applying what we know about rumination to this question. And then you can conduct an N=1 research study on yourself to see if it is effective for you.

Assuming trauma therapists are like educators, we watch more television when we are feeling highly pressured, and we ruminate more when we are watching television than when we are engaged in more active pursuits (Cropley & Millward Purvis, 2003). That isn't a promising beginning. This fact is, however, consistent with what we have learned about the default mode thus far—not being actively engaged results in more rumination. This study provides us more evidence that television watching is an invitation toward rumination *if we are watching passively.*

An older media industry study found, however, that ruminations are reduced when watching cognitively stimulating programming (Bryant & Zillmann, 1984). This study is dated and has limitations, but it aligns with the fact pattern of rumination research and absorbing activities. I would summarize the hypothesis about television watching and rumination this way: If you notice that you are in a rumination loop on one of those evenings when you are simply too exhausted to get involved in some physical activity, watching a television show may be an effective option. It can potentially be that "absorbing activity" that can short circuit the cognitive-emotional link. But *only* if you are: 1) watching with *active* deliberateness, and 2) you have selected programming that absorbs your attention completely. If your arousal is too high, or the programming of too little interest, you need to move to another strategy. Once again, it is all about conscious oversight and deliberateness. Pay attention to what is happening for you and apply active strategies. If it works for you, fantastic. If not, move to another strategy.

The DMN is the self-referential part of the brain. For that reason, activities that take you out of thinking about yourself are the most effective at moving us into task positive mode. The top two activities that Killingworth and Gilbert revealed made us happier than any others, making love and conversation, take us out of the self and redirect our focus toward someone else. The author Anne Lamott said, "My mind is like a bad neighborhood. I try to not go there alone". When you are ruminating, your mind is a bad neighborhood. Maybe you shouldn't stay in there by yourself.

Although some of the neuroanatomical aspects of Stephen Porge's polyvagal theory (2011) have been disputed, he makes observations about the effect of interpersonal relationships upon the parasympathetic response that are beyond dispute. The human stress response begins to resolve—in Porge's terms the vagus nerve is toned—by the sight of another person's eyes and by the sound of the human voice. In other words, when we are communicating with a trusted other, we immediately begin to recover from stress.

That is why I identify conversation as one of the most effective "absorbing activities" to break the rumination cycle. Conversation was second on Killingsworth and Gilbert's list of mood-lifting activities. Conversation is task positive—our attention is focused on the subject of the conversation and the person we are talking with, not the stress event from earlier today. Conversation is other-focused—it takes us out of our own mind (and ruminations). And, conversation tones parasympathetic recovery—it creates in us a sense of safety that allows us to end the fight-or-flight response. This is a critical component of any absorbing activity. By allowing us to physiologically move back into the "green zone", the energy of the rumination-making part of the brain is dissipated.

I had an experience that illustrates the components of this rumination reducing skill set. I was directing a trauma program at a mental health center that exclusively treats preschool-age children. I walked into my office to find the agency's Chief Operating Officer staring intently out my window. She said she was watching a young mother, whose four-year-old son had a bloody nose. The front desk had reported that this mother had struck her young son in the face, and she was determining whether the police and Child Protective Services should be notified. We learned later that this isn't what happened; the boy had struck his nose on the railing of the stairway when he jumped down the final two steps. I didn't know that at the time, which took my stress response to full alert.

I walked outside to check on the boy's status to see if we needed to act. As I opened the front door, I immediately saw a trail of blood drops on the front porch out to the parking lot. This image encoded itself in my mind's eye as a flashbulb memory—I can still recall it vividly. I walked out to find the mother providing good physical care and emotionally soothing the boy. But I was struck by the image of his blood-soaked t-shirt that she had wrapped around his face. At the time, I still believed that she had struck him. For the next half-hour, we worked to calm the boy and to put the pieces of the story together to learn what had happened.

The story had a good ending—the boy's mother had not hit him, and she was able to soothe him for what ultimately was nothing more than a typical childhood accident. But my fight-or-flight stress system had been alerted to the possibility that this was an active child abuse scene, with multiple images of blood.

By the time I got home that evening, I knew that this hadn't been a catastrophic event. But the period of uncertainty and the images of the blood-drop trail and injured little boy continued to intrude in my thinking. I began to ruminate about them.

It took me an hour or more to realize that I was in the rumination cycle. Instead of mentally resolving this as the relatively inconsequential event that it was, I was becoming more and more bothered by the event. The images were intensifying, as was my mental rehearsing whether or not I had handled it properly. It felt like I was just trying to work it out in my mind. Finally, I realized that I was ruminating. In an effort to practice what I preach, I said to myself, "You are just spinning on this. You need to break the recycling".

I decided to do a formal meditation sit. I got out my meditation cushion, set a meditation timer for 20 minutes, and tried to focus on my breath. After the timer went off 20 minutes later, I realized that I hadn't been effective at moving into task-positive mode. I had been conjuring images of the blood on the concrete, the anxiety of whether Mom had or hadn't struck her child, re-imaging the witnesses I talked with, planning a conversation with the Mom's therapist. Instead of moving into task positive mode, I had created a perfect, uninterrupted 20-minute rumination.

Still sitting on my meditation cushion, I acknowledged that I hadn't succeeded. Asking myself what advice I would give to one of the therapists that I supervise who was ruminating, I mentally summoned the list that I outline here. I went downstairs and began a conversation with my partner. I didn't discuss the incident (though that would have been okay), but rather, asked her about her workday. For about 15 minutes we conversed in a very ordinary way. As the conversation wound down, I could feel that I was back in the "green zone". I felt calm.

As I considered why the meditation was ineffective, I concluded it was because by the time I initiated my meditation sit, I was physically agitated. For meditators more skillful than me, meditation might be the best strategy. But I personally need to deal with my physical agitation first before I find meditation to be helpful. So—although after my conversation with my partner I felt that the rumination was resolved—I wanted to move. I leashed my dog and took a brisk 45-minute walk. By the time I returned and for the rest of the evening I was fully in the green zone. I felt calm and was thinking about going back into the office tomorrow with a sense of calm.

My personal example is very quotidian—there was nothing special either about experiencing a stress event or anything I did to reduce my rumination. I would have talked with my partner and walked the dog anyway that evening. What distinguished this strategy—and what made it effective—is the deliberateness with which I was engaging the activities. I was substituting a passive response (being buffeted by rumination) for an active one: 1) I noted that I was distressed; 2) I identified the source of my distress as rumination; 3) I distinguished the rumination from problem solving or "working it out"; 4) I actively decided to do something task-positive to break the cycle; 5) when the meditation failed, I noted that and moved to an external strategy (conversation); 6) noting that I had been experiencing physical agitation, I employed an activity that involved physical movement. My body had been stuck in fight or flight—I needed a small "flee" in order to allow that cycle to complete.

Tenacious Ghosts: When the Ruminations Persist

As I noted, in most situations, the rumination cycle can be short-circuited by interrupting it for as little as two minutes. Sometimes, however, these "ghosts" are more dogged. The tendency to ruminate is much higher is some individuals than in others. Some of us have brains that are "sticky", and some of us have "Teflon brains". You may be speed-reading this chapter because ruminating is not a major source of your secondary traumatic stress. But some therapists are much more predisposed to ruminate. Perhaps their arousal level is higher during the stress event. Perhaps stress takes longer to resolve because of their physiology. Or, perhaps their brains are simply wired to spend more of their time in the default mode. I have created a simple rumination assessment that you can take at the end of this chapter to see where you fall on this tendency. (You probably already know.)

But some ruminations are especially persistent. Maybe—even if you aren't usually predisposed to rumination—a particular stress event was exceptionally provocative. Sometimes the rumination strikes as you are lying in bed trying to go to sleep. Or perhaps it even wakes you in the wee hours of the night. This isn't the time to take your three-mile run or to break out your art supplies in order to interrupt the rumination.

What can you do when late-night or persistent ruminations don't readily resolve? What if the rumination isn't extinguished after the two-minute (or 20-minute) focused activity?

The first strategy for these tenacious ghosts is to treat them as you would an intruding thought during a meditation. During meditation practice, when you are focusing on the breath and a thought intrudes, you are coached to simply acknowledge that you are experiencing a thought and then to return to the breath. The goal is not to become angry with yourself, nor surprised or frustrated that you are ruminating, but to nonjudgmentally acknowledge the thought and return to the breath. In short, the goal is to notice and acknowledge the thought, but not to get yourself worked up about it.

This strategy of gently acknowledging and allowing thoughts to pass can be effective with especially persistent ruminations as well. After you have actively broken the cognitive–emotional link via an active strategy—and you allow your mind to return to default mode—you may again begin to have thoughts of the stress event. This will sometimes occur because the stress event was a profound one. Acknowledge the rumination without emotion or self-criticism, "Oh, I'm ruminating again". Then, simply allow it to pass over as you redirect your focus to whatever you are doing. You want to remain calmly in your "green zone" as you notice it and focus on something else.

If the rumination persists, become aware of the body. Is your heart rate accelerated? Are you breathing fast and shallow? Feeling tension in your chest, or neck? Remember that the rumination cycle is a *cycle*. That means the ruminative thoughts fuel the stress response, but also that the stress response fuels the ruminations. This linkage can be broken from either direction—or ideally, from both directions.

If you aren't successful at reducing arousal by cognitive redirection, you may need to reduce your physiological arousal. One way to do this is through some activity that requires physical movement. A sitting activity like knitting—even if you enjoy it—may not be enough to release your stress response. Because you are in fight or flight, the default mode part of your brain is furiously producing stressful images for you to prepare for. This may make distraction difficult. Your body needs the spike of activity with a discrete beginning and end to know when you are done fighting or fleeing.

Yoga, walking, running, cycling—any type of movement—will initiate a peak, followed by recovery. Remember that this activity can be brief and enjoyable. Ideally, you have some type of physical activity that you enjoy. Remember that relying on willpower to power you through an aversive activity isn't likely to be effective when you are tired and stressed. Engaging in a physical activity that you enjoy, on the other hand, simultaneously focusing the mind away from the default mode ruminations facilitates resolution of the physiological stress response.

Your personal rumination reduction plan needs to be tailored to what works for you and how your brain and body are wired to experience stress. Some people resolve stress quickly and completely and may not be troubled by ruminations very often in the first place. Some feel motivated to move when they are stressed, so they are naturally inclined toward physical activities as an absorbing activity. But some are more inclined to go toward the "freeze" response and feel exhausted, and physical activity is the last thing they are likely to do. If that describes you, focusing on the breath may be easier for you. The important thing is that—when you are experiencing autonomic arousal that makes it difficult to focus on an absorbing task—you find a way to quiet the physiological stress response. Determine which are you most likely to benefit from when you are worrying about the stressful events of the day. Physical activity or focus on the breath?

Some treatment professionals such as Brown and Gerbarg (2009) recommend adding "paced breathing" to meditation to enhance its benefits for stress reduction. Also termed "yogic breathing" or "coherent breathing", this simple technique consists of pacing the breathing to even five-second inhalations and five-second exhalations. This is a pace of six breaths per minute. This pace (and this focus) seems to be very effective at activating parasympathetic recovery and has even been shown to improve heart rate variability (Lin et al., 2014). The Tibetan mantra "Om Mani Padme Hum" chanted on the exhale, with equal time allotted for the inhalation, results in approximately six complete breaths per minute. Interestingly, reciting the Ave Maria in Latin also results in the same breath cycle (Bernardi et al., 2001), suggesting the possibility these cross-cultural practices evolved for the purpose of creating meditative states by controlled respiration.

I am not promoting a particular chant/prayer, nor a particular pacing of the breath. There are scores of breathing practices that support paced breathing: 4–7–8 breathing, alternate nostril breathing, equal breathing, four-square breathing. Rather than promoting a specific approach, I offer these as just a few examples of ways to absorb the mind away from the rumination when fight-or-flight arousal is high.

I am, however, promoting that—if you are troubled by persistent ruminations—you identify some strategy that can create a state of absorption away from the default mode even when you are in fight or flight. The breath is the gateway between conscious thought and autonomic response—it can be controlled by thought, but also happens without thought. That is why focus upon the breath has been employed in spiritual practices for thousands of years. Any of these strategies can be effective when other, simpler distractions have been ineffective.

Nighttime Ruminations

Sometimes distressing ruminations occur as we are trying to go to sleep. As you lay in bed without the distractions of daytime activity, suddenly you think of the stress event that you experienced today. The middle of the night—when you aren't focused on any activity except trying to sleep—is a likely time for the mental looping that comprises rumination. As you lie in the dark with only you and your thoughts, these mental images are difficult to halt. And these thoughts are only fueled more by your rising anxiety that you are losing sleep and going to be exhausted the next day. You are in a dilemma: if you turn on a light (or blue screen) your sleep cycle will be disrupted, and it will be harder to sleep. If you don't turn on a screen or light, you are left in the dark—alone with your ruminations.

Rumination-Focused Cognitive Behavioral Therapy makes a contrast between ruminations and what they term ACES (not to be confused with Felitti's Adverse Childhood Events). ACES refers to the four characteristics of problem-solving based thinking: Action, Concrete, Experiential, and Specific (Watkins, 2018). Problem-based thinking is all of those things: action-focused, concrete, specific, and directly engaged in experience. Ruminations, on the other hand, tend to be passive re-experiencing of the stress event and past-focused, whereas problem solving is future focused.

The ACES concept provides us with a tool we can use for those nighttime ruminations. The goal is to move our thinking from the general, repetitive ruminations towards ACES thinking. This is something we can do without getting out of bed, and without waking our partner. And—even in the effort to put the stress event into an ACES plan, we are engaging in task-positive action. That puts us half-way there!

Let's use my personal experience of the four-year-old boy with the bloody nose. For sake of illustration, imagine that I awaken at 3:00 AM with the images of this little boy and the blood drop trail. After a few moments, I realize that the images have activated my stress response and I don't feel like I will be able to go back to sleep. The images intrude in my mind, followed by my mental review of the things I did and conversations that I had with the people involved. First—as always—I must catch myself. So, I note that I am ruminating and that this is not productive nor sleep inducing. I don't want to be passive as I wait the rumination out, so I select an active response (but one that doesn't require me to turn on the light.)

The "A" in ACES refers to an action. Consistent with CE-CERT principles, active responses are substituted for passive responses. During the rumination imagery, I am passively exposed to the stress event over and over again. I'm not really doing anything. The first step in moving to problem-focused thinking is to ask myself, "What action do I need to take?" This is also a useful question if you are trying to decide if you are in productive problem-focused thinking or if you are ruminating. If there is not action you can or need to take, you are probably in non-productive rumination.

In my example, I had taken all the actions I needed to take before I left the office that day. The rumination was simply intrusive images, and not an action demand. In that case, my action is to review the situation with specificity. In this example, I will decide that the action I need to take is to supportively communicate to those involved that "all is well". I want to make sure that the mother knows that we do not suspect her and that she handled the situation well. I communicated that to her today, but I will choose to communicate with her again tomorrow to add further assurance. I also want to briefly talk to the boy just as a check in on his well-being after his incident. I also want to communicate with the front desk workers and the child's therapist to let them know how well the situation was managed. Because all of these communications are positive and supportive messages, this has the added benefit of moving me into a compassionate mode, which allows parasympathetic response. My stress begins to resolve. This planning is all happening mentally, as I have decided to keep the lights off. These planned communications are the actions that comprise the "A" of the ACES.

As I continue to lie still, I continue my ACES. The action is that I will talk with the mother, the child, and three of my staff members. Bear in mind that the quality of rumination is general and emotion focused. Therefore, the C/E/S part of my plan is to form specific and precise details of what I will do tomorrow rather than on a general summary. "I have a break from clinical meetings at 10:30. I will call the boy's mother, and this is what I will say... Once I am satisfied that I have communicated support to her, I will ask if her son could talk for a moment..." And so on—until my plan is fully formed at a very specific, concrete level.

Consider what is happening as you do this ACES planning. You are now focused on the plan ("What did the ACES stand for?" "What should my action be?" "Is this a concrete action?"). This kind of thinking is task positive—I am already interrupting the rumination cycle. Because this is planning, it is future oriented. Future orientation is the opposite of ruminative rehashing of past events. It is an action plan, which is active and empowering in contrast to being passively buffeted by rumination as I lie in bed. And finally, it provides concrete reason for me to feel that I have done all that I need to do right now—and that I know exactly what I will do tomorrow. I can consider it finished. The stress can resolve.

You know yourself well enough to know if you need to commit this plan to writing—although it requires a light to be turned on. Some people can articulate the plan better in writing, and the act of writing seems to pin the worry to the page. Consider this if you are having difficulty focusing the mind. For some, being able to focus the anxiety and pin it to the page may allow them to turn off the light and return to sleep.

Reducing Ruminations Is Learning How to Complete the Stress Event

Consider for a moment the enormity of the concept we have covered in this chapter. Some of you have less reactive systems and are rarely troubled by ruminations in the evenings and on the weekend. Some of you have stress responses that are more reactive and take longer to resolve. If the latter describes you, you are more likely to be troubled by ruminations—your stress lasts longer. But for all readers of this page, the practices and skills I have described here have very significant application. Not just application for work events that become evening ruminations, but for life stress in general.

I am certainly not the first one to describe the human brain as a hormone gland. As Sapolsky says, "I can think a thought and my pancreas secretes a hormone—and I don't even know where the pancreas is". And, of course, the stress response works the other direction as well. This cascade of hormones initiated by the brain also affects the brain itself—in ways temporary and in ways that rewire the brain. The skill of consciously tending the thoughts that are causing us distress is a high skill indeed, with profound potential. Potential not only to mediate the effects of intrusive ruminations, but to alter the effect of stress on us more generally.

I introduced CE-CERT in the first chapter as an assemblage of skills that provide conscious control over our autonomic responses. Reducing ruminations is, in essence, learning to "exhale" after a stress event. It is letting the stress be finished when the stress event is finished in fact. This allows the body to recover (the parasympathetic recovery can begin), protects us from the effects of chronic stress (experiencing stress as a time-limited event rather than a constant "stress bath"), and allows me to be more present in what is now in front of me. Who doesn't need that skill?

If I have had an evening without distress from the stress events and trauma exposure of my workday, it bodes well for my evening. If I sleep well because I am not conjuring stress and trauma images, I will be more rested. And all of that makes it much easier to go into work the next day.

Reducing Rumination: How to Prevent Bad Moments from Ruining the Whole Day

You Must Remember This

• *What Is Rumination?*

- Ruminations occur when we get stuck in thinking about a stressful situation. When we are ruminating, we are still thinking about (and therefore still feeling stress about) situations hours or even days after a stressful event.

- When we get emotionally "worked up" in response to a remembered stress event, the brain creates even more mental images, which leads to more physical arousal, etc. Now we are stuck in a cycle between our imaging and the stress response. And if we are ruminating, we are less present for our next client, our family, or our next activity.

- Research has shown that the more time we spend in rumination, the less happy and effective we are. Rumination then, is the exact opposite of being present in the moment (mindfulness).

• *Why Do We Ruminate?*

- The propensity to ruminate is determined by two factors: 1) how we experience the level of threat in the circumstance, and 2) how quickly our physiological make-up allows us to recover.

- Some of us recover quickly and rarely ruminate. Others take longer to recover from a stressful event, and rumination is a near daily occurrence. Most workers in the helping professions, however, at least occasionally contend with ruminations about stressful situations.

Bridging Concepts to Skills: Banishing the Ghosts That Follow

Even if you have a high propensity towards rumination, you can get better at putting stressful situations behind and staying present:

1. *Know the Difference Between Problem Solving and Ruminating*

- Healthy problem solving is when we feel like we can do something about a stressful situation and are trying to define an action. When we are problem solving, we feel empowered and are focused on what to *do* about the situation.

- Rumination, on the other hand, is when we are focused on how unpleasant the situation was, and we can't do anything to resolve it. Rather than focusing on what we should *do*, we focus on how we *feel*.

- The first step in reducing a rumination is to get better at noticing when you are ruminating. If you have difficulty knowing whether you are problem solving or ruminating, ask yourself this question, "Is there something I need to do about this situation?"

2. *Notice and Label When You Are Ruminating*

   • When you become aware that you are stuck in a thought or image of a stressful event, signal to yourself that you are ruminating so you can take deliberate action.

3. *Actively Avoid Mind-Wandering*

   • Decide to change your mental state with deliberateness.

4. *Short-Circuit the Imaging/Emotional Reacting Circuit for As Little as Two Minutes*

   • For normal ruminations, a complete focus on something else as little as two minutes can do the trick (when done with deliberateness).

5. *Converse with Someone*

   • This simple action can be very effective at ending a rumination and interrupting the self-perpetuating loop.
   • Furthermore, engaging in a conversation with a person we like and with whom we feel safe, activates parasympathetic recovery and helps us return to our emotional and physical baseline.

6. *Consciously Engage in an Absorbing Activity*

   • Any activity that effectively holds your attention away from the rumination—and away from your own self-referential thoughts—will break the self-perpetuating circuit of the rumination.
   • For most of us, it will need to be something more active or engaging than merely watching a television show or our attention will flip back and forth between the show and our rumination, allowing the ruminative circuit to continue.

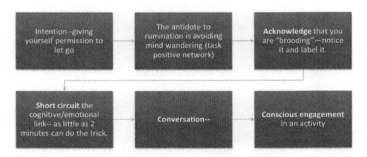

Reducing Rumination: Resting the Mind

Rumination Scale

On a *typical* day:

1. *When I'm doing things that allow my mind to wander, such as driving, cleaning, or trying to fall asleep, I think about stressful situations from my job.*

1. Never	2. Rarely	3. Sometimes	4. Often	5. All the time

2. *I find it difficult to relax because the stressful thoughts about work seem to come into my mind even more when I'm still.*

1. Never	2. Rarely	3. Sometimes	4. Often	5. All the time

3. *I wake up in the middle of the night unable to get back to sleep because I can't stop thinking about a conflict or problem at work.*

1. Never	2. Rarely	3. Sometimes	4. Often	5. All the time

4. When I think about difficult clients, my thoughts are more likely to go to:

1. Re-hashing the event that upset me	2. Defining a concrete solution	3. How upset I feel

5. *After a stressful event at work, which group best represents your response in the evening?* (Circle "A" or "B")

(a)	(b)
I thought about the event when I did not mean to. Thoughts about the event came to mind and I could not stop thinking about them. Thoughts about the event distracted me or kept me from being able to concentrate. Even in the late evening my thoughts were returning to the event.	I was able to fully focus on what I was doing that evening. If I thought about the event, it was because I deliberately summoned it up. When I thought about the event, I felt thoughtful and calm. I thought about whether I have learned anything as a result of my experience.

6. You just finished an interaction with a client who was irrationally angry at you and presented complex problems that made it hard for you to know what to do. Predict how long it will take to return to a calm, baseline emotional state:

    1. Less than 1 hour
    2. Less than 4 hours
    3. The rest of the day
    4. Could last for more than a day

Rumination Scale
Self-Scoring

> 1. Enter your response in the left column.
>
> 2. Follow the instructions in the center column to translate your score to the "resulting score" column.
>
> 3. Add the entries in the right column to calculate your score.

Your entered score	Convert Score Instructions	Resulting Score
1.	1 Transfer your actual score to the next column:	
2.	2. Transfer your actual score to the next column:	
3.	3. Transfer your actual score to the next column:	
4.	4. If you answered 1, enter 4: If you answered 2, enter 0: If you answered 3, enter 4:	
5.	5. If you answered A, enter 4: If you answered B, enter 0:	
6.	6. Transfer your actual score to the next column:	
	Total	

0-8	You are a low ruminator. Rumination is not typically a source of stress for you.
9-20	You are a "circumstantial ruminator". Your tendency to ruminate is directly related to how intense the exposure to the stress event was.
21-30	You are a high ruminator. You are likely to have frequent ruminations in the evenings and weekends. You react strongly to stressors, and your physiology may be slow to return to baseline. It will be critical for you to develop skillfulness in managing your tendency to ruminate.

Reducing Rumination

Self-Audit

Gray	I rarely carry emotions or images of difficult situations for more than a few moments.
Light Gray	I find myself ruminating about something from work when I am home after something especially stressful happens.
Black	Most evenings and weekends I am ruminating about work.

References

Bernardi, L., Sleight, P., Bandinelli, G., Cencetti, S., Fattorini, L., Wdowczyc-Szulc, J., & Lagi, A. (2001). Effect of rosary prayer and yoga mantras on autonomic cardiovascular rhythms: Comparative study. *British Medical Journal, 323*(7327), 1446–1449.

Brown, R. P., & Gerbarg, P. L. (2009). Yoga breathing, meditation, and long-evity. *Annals of the New York Academy of Sciences, 1172*(1), 54.

Bryant, J., & Zillmann, D. (1984). Using television to alleviate boredom and stress: Selective exposure as a function of induced excitational states. *Journal of Broadcasting & Electronic Media, 28*(1), 1–20.

Buckner, R. L., Andrews-Hanna, J. R., & Schacter, D. L. (2008). The brain's default network: Anatomy, function, and relevance to disease. *Annals of the New York Academy of Sciences, 1124*, 1–38.

Cropley, M., & Millward Purvis, L. (2003). Job strain and rumination about work issues during leisure time: A diary study. *European Journal of Work and Organizational Psychology, 12*(3), 195–207.

Deng, Y. Q., Li, S., & Tang, Y. Y. (2014). The relationship between wandering mind, depression and mindfulness. *Mindfulness, 5*(2), 124–128.

Killingsworth, M. A., & Gilbert, D. T. (2010). A wandering mind is an unhappy mind. *Science, 330*(6006), 932–932.

LeFevre, J. (1988). Flow and the quality of experience during work and leisure. In M. Csikszentmihalyi & I. S. Csikszentmihalyi (Eds.), *Optimal experience: Psychological studies of flow in consciousness*. New York: Harper & Row.

Lin, I. M., Tai, L. Y., & Fan, S. Y. (2014). Breathing at a rate of 5.5 breaths per minute with equal inhalation-to-exhalation ratio increases heart rate variability. *International Journal of Psychophysiology, 91*(3), 206–211.

Lutz, A., Brefczynski-Lewis, J., Johnstone, T., & Davidson, R. J. (2008). Regulation of the neural circuitry of emotion by compassion meditation: Effects of meditative expertise. *PloS One, 3*(3).

Merriam-Webster. (n.d.). *Rumination*. In Merriam-Webster.com dictionary. Retrieved August 22, 2020, from https://www.merriam-webster.com/dictionary/rumination.

Patterson, D. W., (Ed.). (2008). *John Cage: Music, philosophy, and intention, 1933–1950*. New York: Routledge.

Porges, S. W. (2011). *The polyvagal theory: Neurophysiological foundations of emotions, attachment, communication, and self-regulation*. New York: W.W. Norton.

Radomsky, A. S., Alcolado, G. M., Abramowitz, J. S., Alonso, P., Belloch, A., Bouvard, M., & Garcia-Soriano, G. (2014). Part 1—You can run but you can't hide: Intrusive thoughts on six continents. *Journal of Obsessive-Compulsive and Related Disorders, 3*(3), 269–279.

Ruby, F. J., Smallwood, J., Engen, H., & Singer, T. (2013). How self-generated thought shapes mood—the relation between mind-wandering and mood depends on the socio-temporal content of thoughts. *PloS One, 8*(10).

Sapolsky, R. M. (2004). *Why zebras don't get ulcers: A guide to stress, stress related diseases, and coping* (3rd ed.). New York: W.H. Freeman.

Smallwood, J., Fitzgerald, A., Miles, L. K., & Phillips, L. H. (2009). Shifting moods, wandering minds: Negative moods lead the mind to wander. *Emotion, 9*(2), 271.

Watkins, E. R. (2018). *Rumination-focused cognitive-behavioral therapy for depression*. New York: Guilford Publications.

4 Stories of the Quest: The Antecedent Narrative

Conscious Narrative: Telling Our Story

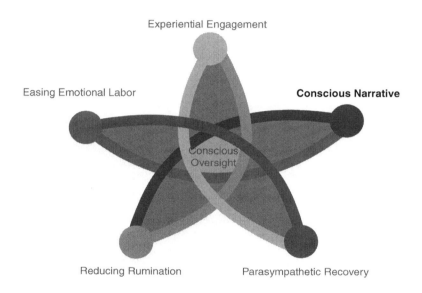

If you have built castles in the air, your work need not be lost; that is where they should be. Now put the foundations under them.

Henry David Thoreau

Telling the Story of Our Work

A thought experiment: After years of wanting to do so, you finally make a trip to Yellowstone National Park. After a long day on the plane and the two-hour drive from the Idaho Falls Airport, you arrive at your rental cabin. Excited to finally be in the park on a beautiful day, you say to your partner, "Let's not even unpack right now—let's go take a hike before it gets dark". But your partner is less ambitious than you are and replies, "No, I've almost finished reading my chapter in this book. I just want to have a cup of tea and settle in here. You go ahead without me".

And so, you do. You find a lovely hiking path that leads through the pines. Walking along the trail you are in an outstandingly good mood—the smell of pine, perfect walking temperature, and blue cloudless skies combine to put you in a wonderful, mindful state. Until, that is, you walk into a clearing leading to a meadow. Here, your reverie is interrupted by the sight of a grizzly no less than 40 yards away, who has risen on his hind legs and is growling in terrorizing menace as he looks directly at you. You instinctively turn and run at full speed back down the trail you were walking. (This book is about contending with secondary traumatic stress, not solid advice about wilderness safety.) You are fortunate, and the grizzly does not pursue you. But, nonetheless, you run at full sprint all the way back to your cabin. Arriving there, you slam the door shut and—just to be safe—lock and bolt the door. You are still breathing heavily and trying to absorb what just happened when you partner says, "Oh, that was fast. How was your walk?"

Now to the heart of the thought experiment: imagine—really imagine—that this is your response: "Oh, it was nice. I decided to come back early, but the weather couldn't have been better. Perfect temperature, not a cloud in the sky, nice trail for hiking". In other words, imagine talking about anything *except* the bear. *Don't say anything about the grizzly.*

If you get inside that thought experiment, you will have the sensation that every cell in your body cries out for you to "tell them about what just happened with the grizzly!" And herein lies the question: why do we have an almost physical need to tell this story?

Here is the principle illustrated by the thought experiment: *intense experiences demand a narrative.* Whenever we have an experience that causes strong feelings of any kind, we will have a potent drive to describe it to someone. At an almost cellular level, those feelings need us to tell the story before they can resolve. Why is that—why do we have such a strong impulse to tell someone about the extraordinary things that happen to us? It is clear that, in the literal sense, our brain has evolved to create narratives, and, importantly, our parasympathetic system requires narratives to resolve intense feelings.

Narratives Harmonize the Left and Right Hemispheres of the Brain

Daniel Siegel (2007) discusses how accurately describing our feelings harmonizes the hemispheres of the brain. Inchoate images of the event, and feelings about that event, arise in the right hemisphere, but the language center of the brain in in the left hemisphere. As the cliché "name it to tame it" suggests, the stress begins to resolve when accurate labels (left hemisphere) are placed on strong feelings (right hemisphere). When we put it into words, right and left hemispheres begin to align.

In other words, the fight-or-flight response resolves when we simultaneously *summon* the memory and *tell the story* about the memory.

In the research world, "name it to tame it" is referred to as "affect labeling". Accurate labeling of our emotions has been shown to increase activity in the pre-frontal cortex, which dampens activity in the amygdala, the alarm center of the brain (Creswell et al., 2007; Torrisi et al., 2013). This is the central principle of psychotherapy: putting words to our feelings. When we do, limbic arousal is reduced, and pre-frontal thinking enhanced. And—importantly—when we fail to tell our story, our feelings get "acted out" in ways that are uncomfortable and even destructive. Words are, as Rudyard Kipling (n.d.) said, "the most powerful drug used by mankind".

Narratives Situate Us in Time

Consider what happens when you tell the story of the grizzly to your partner: This is you, in the safety of the cabin, telling them the story of what happened in the recent past. You are situating yourself in the here and now. You are safe, not in mortal danger from the grizzly. You are telling the story *now*, not living the terror of *then*. Your narrative places the "file" of this event in its proper place in time and space as you tell its story. "I am here as the teller of this story". Now you can begin to recover. You are safe. And you have a new anecdote.

Narratives Place Events in Context

As you create your narrative about the bear, your brain begins placing it in context. The hippocampal portion of our brain encodes the stress event as an "event memory", containing facts and places relating to that event. But neural associations must be established with higher brain functions before that event has meaning. That is exactly what you are doing as you create your narrative—you are weaving the event memories (hippocampus) as you activate the left temporal cortex by telling a story. This allows the neocortex to incorporate the event into the larger context of your life. Once incorporated, you now know what to do with the experience (carry bear spray, don't run away next time, make more noise along the trail, or go to the Greek Islands instead of a Western forest.) As or La Guin suggested, stories are "our only boat for sailing on the river of time" (2014).

Narratives Connect Us with Others

And last, stories are potent social connectors. We are in the second act of our journey learning how to mitigate the effects of secondary trauma. Imagine that we are sitting around the fire with our tribe, telling stories.

You are not alone, terrified on the trail as you run from the bear. You are with your people, sharing the tale of an exciting adventure. The stressor has been transformed from a moment of solitary terror to a shared adventure. In this place—telling stories with people you trust—is where you recover from the stress event. When we are with people who we trust—and when our stressful experiences are fully contextualized—we feel better. Our parasympathetic system moves toward full recovery when we feel safe among our own.

Stress events are constantly occurring in trauma work. And so are our narratives. Not all of our stressful experiences are as dramatic as the encounter with the grizzly. And we may not even be aware of our narrative about those events—the stories write themselves without us thinking much about it. These narratives are constant, but they are not always *conscious*. We may create narratives that erode our motivation and stress resilience, or we might create narratives that sustain a rewarding career in trauma work. It depends upon how we tell those stories to ourselves. We must tell these stories properly.

Hannah Gadsby is a comedian and trauma survivor/storyteller. In her performance "Nannette", she states that she has decided she must quit comedy (she didn't). She must quit comedy, she says, because comedy is told in two acts: the comedian creates tension, and then the comedian makes the audience laugh to release the tension. But—as she accurately points out—real-life stories require three acts—not just tension and release, but a beginning, middle, and end. She is citing an empirical fact. "You learn from the part of the story you focus on", she says. "I need to tell my story properly" (Bruzzese et al., 2018).

This chapter is about telling your story properly. And telling the story of your work properly doesn't rely on bromides or positive affirmations. Your narrative cannot be built on false sunshine in which you try to convince yourself that your work isn't every bit as hard as it is. In fact, telling your story properly is very much about hewing *closer* to the truth of your work.

I sometimes refer to the conscious narrative as "cognitive behavioral therapy for therapists". Because cognitive behavioral therapy (CBT) is, ultimately, about correcting irrational thoughts (narratives) and substituting healthier thought patterns. In your role as therapist, some narratives will make it harder for you to come to work each day, will reduce your stress resilience, and will make your work seem pointless. Other narratives will open you to the events of the day, will increase your stress hardiness, and will make your work deeply and personally meaningful. In very real ways, Rukeyser (n.d.) was correct when she said that "The universe is made of stories, not of atoms".

I promise I'm not leading up to a proposal that you put Post-it Notes on your mirror with affirming messages to chant while you get ready for work. Rather, I am going to guide you toward paying more attention to the story you tell yourself about your work, and intentionally cultivating narrative themes that support hardiness and purpose. These narratives must be based in reality, and—importantly—they will also affect our reality. We don't want to passively let our story write us—our goal must be to actively author the narrative of our work.

I have been using "story" and "narrative" interchangeably heretofore, but now I must make a distinction. "Story" refers to the events that happened. The story is just the facts of the matter. Telling your story properly doesn't mean changing or even glossing over these facts. Contrariwise, telling our story properly requires a scrupulous noticing of the truth. The "narrative" is how you organize the story and your choices in putting it together—what you emphasize and what you deemphasize. The narrative refers to the editorial decisions you make that determine which parts of the story you put a positive valence upon and what parts you place a negative valence upon. We can stay within the truth and still make important narrative choices. Some choices will sustain us. The *conscious* narrative is being aware of the choices you have made. It is deciding to tell your story and not letting your story just happen to you.

The importance of narrative is one reason that this book is outlined in the classic three-act structure. This chapter is occurring within those three acts but also contains its own three acts. Telling our story properly requires all three acts. In order to prepare for and to recover from stress events, our brain seeks a beginning, a middle, and an end—the three acts. And within each of those acts, certain narratives can be cultivated to sustain us in a long career in trauma work, and certain narratives will wreak havoc upon our sense of engagement and meaning.

The Antecedent Narrative

As I mentioned in the previous chapter, all day long we are talking to ourselves in our heads. The antecedent narrative refers to that part of our narrative comprised of the background commentary that is running much of the time. This commentary is sort of the "podcast" narration that we recite to ourselves as we anticipate our day. The antecedent narrative is the "before" part of the story. When we anticipate events beforehand, we naturally place a positive or negative valence on those events as we expect them. And that valence—the positive or negative value that you place on it—can change everything.

The antecedent narrative also contains those deep, embedded stories that you have incorporated to explain yourself and your world—the big conclusions you have made about yourself, your world, your job. In CBT, cognitive schemas are those foundational beliefs that play a central role in how functional or dysfunctional your worldview is. In developmental psychology, schemas can be described as the building blocks for knowledge acquisition. For our purposes here, schemas are the building blocks for our narratives. These schemas filter what we notice, what we include, and what we overlook from the "grand narrative" of our work. These foundational narratives will strongly affect the way we experience events—in some cases defining our experience more than the actual events themselves.

The antecedent narrative is, in the simplest terms, what we tell ourselves before any event. This before-the-fact narrative includes your deeply held worldview (schema) and your expectations about this immediate event. The antecedent narrative includes all the things you were saying to yourself before you went to work last Thursday. It includes whether you looked forward to that day with positive anticipation (a positive valence) or with dread (a negative valence.) These valences—positive or negative—were based upon larger conclusions you have made about your work in the organization, your tasks, your clients, and your co-workers. It even includes the deeper conclusions about what is—and is what is not—enjoyable. You did a lot more work last Thursday before you even left for the office than you realized!

So, let's look at these two elements of the antecedent narrative:

Expectations and Priming

The antecedent narrative is running in your head as you anticipate your day and will have a large effect on how you experience that day. I could take us deep into the Bayesian concept of how our perceptions are formed by the brain weaving together our preexisting beliefs with the sensory input of our lived experience. I could describe how, at the neural level, one group of neurons encode sensory evidence and another group represents our beliefs, and how we synthesize this information into perception (Zhang et al., 2018). But what would take chapters to describe at a complex, neuroanatomical level can also be told more simply. After all, this chapter is about stories. And, as Brené Brown said, "Maybe stories are just data with soul" (Gallo, 2013). The simplest way to describe this aspect of the narrative is that the "podcast" that you are running every morning will have a significant priming effect on how you experience the day.

You know by now how important it is that you open to experience rather than closing off or avoiding intensity. Your antecedent narrative plays a critical role here—are you opening up to the day's experiences as that podcast rolls, or are you "clenching" against the anticipated stress? Here is an example of what opening looks like: "I am curious about what will happen today". Here is a (common) example of what armoring up looks like: "It's Thursday. I've just got to get through today and to-morrow..." It follows rather obviously that it will be harder to engage the day with a "soft front and strong back" if you are clenching against stress before the stress has even happened. Note that by clenching against an-ticipated stress, *you are manufacturing stress in preparation for stress.*

The psychology of narrative—indeed the neurobiology of the brain—demonstrates clearly that words impart a profound psychological effect. Examining your before-work narrative, are you describing yourself as more of a "happy warrior" or more of a "flogged soldier"? Are you approaching the day with open engagement, or with defensive protection? Even as you apply one of those terms to yourself, you are telling—and perhaps changing—a narrative.

To illustrate the priming effect, consider the difference between your experience tasting an intense food or beverage—limburger cheese, caviar, or aged scotch—if you expect it to be intense, compared to expecting something sweet. You would hate the tanginess, saltiness, or astringency if you were only willing to eat sweet things. Much of training your mind and palate for these culinary experiences is priming yourself for "it is supposed to taste (smell) like that". Without priming, you would avoid anything that smelled like limburger cheese. Or anything as salty and fishy as caviar. Or as astringent as scotch. In short, people who enjoy intense foods open up to the intensity and even go deeper into to it to notice subtleties of the flavor at a very granular level. Your childhood palate would not be primed for those experiences. A child's narrative is that food should taste like this to be delicious (sweet and non-complex) and food that tastes like that (smelly and intense) is yucky. You have to expect and welcome intensity to enjoy such foods.

Using the same narrative language, working in the trauma field will be unpleasant if you are only willing to taste things that are sweet and non-complex. Remember that same narrative prompt when we are opening to taste something unfamiliar or intense: "it is supposed to be this way" (smell funky, taste intensely, look slimy). That priming concept allows us to open to engage something we may naturally avoid. We experience more, and we experience it better. We open to "the whole staying and excitement..." (James, 2013).

At the very least, this narrative priming opens us to experience the stress event without all of the stress-before-the-stress that we add by dreading the possibility of intensity. And at best, we may even find some of these stress events to be surprisingly rewarding. We might actually come to like caviar.

Metaphors are an important editorial choice in our narrative—the particular metaphor that we select will have a great effect on how we prime ourselves for facing each event and each day. I selected "flogged soldier" as a metaphor because of its negative valence. Nobody wants to be a flogged soldier, and nobody wants to live their life that way. I selected "happy warrior" because of its unambiguously positive connotation. Maybe you had to begrudgingly admit that you approach work as more of a flogged soldier than a happy warrior. But you would never set being a flogged soldier as an intentional goal. And—as you will see shortly—I will emphasize the importance of setting intentions with our narratives.

I self-reflected about my priming narrative in my job role as director of children's behavioral health at a children's hospital. I was curious about why—since I enjoyed most of the tasks that I engaged in each day, and the children and colleagues I worked with—I often found myself driving into the office with an inchoate sense of dread. This sense was a complete disconnect from the reality that I experienced most days. As I reflected, I realized that my mind—and therefore body—was preparing for the worst experiences. It took a while each day for me to unthaw and begin to enjoy what I was actually engaged in. I began to do a little priming each day as I drove into my office using a variation of the Dr. Mohrmann quote, "I am willing to have my heart broken today..." I had realized that I was armoring up against such heartbreak, and I wanted to open to the possibility. Without intending to, I eventually advanced my mantra to "I *hope* to have my heart broken today..." Although having one's heart broken is painful, I knew if it happened, it meant I was open to feeling whatever feelings were evoked this day.

Narratives are important because they develop a vocabulary for directing our actions. This vocabulary allows us to set an intention that will consolidate into a specific action. Without such a vocabulary, we will unconsciously "act out" in the form of job dissatisfaction or—in the worst case—poor performance on the job. We need a vocabulary even to know what is wrong on our job. We need a vocabulary to know what we are aiming for. We need a vocabulary to tell our story. This story becomes a narrative that directs our job satisfaction.

Foundational Narratives

There is an anonymous saying—often apocryphally credited to Ronald Reagan—that "Some people wonder all their lives if they've made a difference. The Marines don't have that problem". If you have consciously cultivated your narrative, you don't have that problem either. You work to alleviate suffering of another human being. You have the capability to transform trauma into growth. You have the luxury of having a vocation in which *no one can question that what you do has meaning*. But I fear that you only think about the difference that you are making when you read a passage such as this, or when you attend a conference. How personally affected you are by the drive to make a difference—and how connected you remain to that purpose—will potently affect your willingness to engage in your work, and how you experience the stress events within it. If you are doubting that what you do makes a difference, stress and trauma exposure will certainly affect you negatively.

An essential foundational schema is that you believe—deeply and in a felt way—in the importance of your work. Everyone in the helping professions will profess that they do this work because they want to help others. But it is those who feel a connection to that purpose *deeply* and *often* that are doing well in their roles. Sri Nisargadatta Maharaj said that, "the mind creates the abyss, the heart crosses it" (Maharaj, 2017). We must feel the purpose of our jobs in an embodied way to cross the abyss of how difficult and painful the work can be. Our clients can't be merely characters in our personal fiction. We can't just say it or think it; we must *feel* it. And for those for whom this sense of purpose is only a concept—as opposed to a deeply experienced connection—or those who are consumed by mere survival in their job—this sense of purpose must be conscientiously cultivated into a foundational narrative.

You recite a foundational narrative to others when they ask you why you do what you do for a living. You have a narrative that you employed when you had your job interview in response to the question "What is your interest in this position?" If you were giving a talk at a professional conference entitled "Why This Work Matters", you'd have a pretty good idea what you would say.

But here is the challenge: when was the last time that you felt an emotional connection to that purpose statement *while you were doing the work*? Was it yesterday? Did you think of it once last week? At least once last month? All of us have a narrative about the importance of our work. But the busy-ness and—frankly—the monotony of some of our work, takes us away from this narrative.

In order to tell our story properly, we have to remember our story. And we need to tell that story on purpose—to ourselves as well as to others. Those who thrive in long careers in this work have a personal sense of meaning in it. I'm not proposing a Pollyanna view of the nature of your job. Indeed, I would be doing you a disservice if I suggested that your days would be filled with dramatic moments of miraculous changes in clients, and a never-ending sense of gratitude and joy. No one has a job like that, and your narrative won't sustain it. A career-sustaining narrative is one that brings you closer to the truth, not one that fills your head with platitudes. No one can question the meaning in what you do—because it is so utterly *true*. So, if you aren't telling that narrative—if you aren't *feeling* that what you do is making a difference—we want to align the narrative to be more in keeping with this reality.

Let's describe the truth: *sometimes* you are honored to witness profound change in your clients. *Sometimes* you are gratified to feel that you played a role in that change—their life is different because you did your job well. But sometimes you are frustrated and feel unsuccessful. And more often than either of those feelings, you have moments of busy work and even moments of boredom. That is true of even the best jobs. So—although it is critical that you cultivate a narrative of the importance of your work, you must also prime a sense of openness to whatever is going to happen this day. I don't know what that will be. Perhaps it will be profound and will remind you of why you do this work. Perhaps it will be exquisitely painful. Or maybe, it will be downright boring.

We love adages. We put them on t-shirts, bumper stickers, and posters. When one resonates with you, perhaps you print it out and tape it somewhere you will see it. Maybe, if it is good enough, you will put it below your email signature line. You want to be reminded of it, associated with it. Perhaps it speaks to the way you want to define yourself. Perhaps it is aspirational. Like many authors, I introduce each chapter with relevant epigrams. When I give talks at conferences, I rarely get requests for citations for the research that I referenced during my talk. I get requests for some quote that I used that the person found motivating. These quotes stir us—they motivate us.

What those adages—we call them "sayings"—are *saying* is part of our narrative. Think of them as little statements of purpose. They are priming narratives—they give us a vocabulary for what we are aiming for. They open us to an action that relates to what they have stirred in us, for example, "...be the change you wish to see in the world".

The aphorisms with which you resonate tell you something about your cognitive schema—something in that quote connects with some conclusion you have made about the world. That is your animating energy. The fact that you want to remember them, think about them, and share them reveals an intention toward a career-promoting energy. A feeling is primed within that aphorism that you seek as you do your work.

Consider the difference in how I will experience working with an "unmotivated" client based on my narrative frame. (Describing a client as "unmotivated" is already an important narrative choice.) Let's say that I am working with a client who has repeatedly missed appointments and often rejects or argues with my therapeutic efforts. Now assume that you have a deep belief in the aphorism "heaven helps those who help themselves". "I am doing all the work here", I tell myself. "I have led her to the water, now she has to decide if she is going to drink"—another metaphor that will determine my action. Now I adopt a passive waiting role—it is up to her... In another version of the same scenario, I have a different worldview. This time, my underlying dictum is "Everyone is trying the best they can". "I wonder why she feels so stuck—is it fear? Or is it resistance to authority that has taken advantage of her over her entire life? Is she depressed and unable to make decisions? Is she so anxious she can't carry out a plan? I wonder what battle is going on within her..."

The narrative that you select will determine your actions. And that narrative, in turn, may derive from a deeper, foundational narrative that you have internalized, e.g., "My mother always told me that heaven helps those who help themselves".

The focus of this book is mitigating the effects of doing trauma therapy and increasing the pleasure of our work. Consider the previous example from that perspective. It is demoralizing to work harder than your clients. It is discouraging to work hard on behalf of clients whom you resent. Your narrative is going to play a determinative role in how your energy and morale will hold when you encounter clients who are "resistant" or "unmotivated", as compared to "I wonder what battle she is fighting deep inside?"

Cultivating a narrative of personal meaning also must include savoring when those rewarding moments happen. Savoring occurs when we form and when we tell a narrative. I don't want to miss a single one of those rewarding moments that allow me to savor "Yes, this is why I do this". I want to get better at noticing these moments. They constitute the evidence we need that "Yes, I am making a difference".

Consider how differently I will experience the demands of trauma work if my narrative has increasingly sounded like this: "I should have chosen one of those jobs where I work in a nicer office and go out for two-martini lunches". Compare that to a central schema such as the one expressed by Sue Fitzmaurice (n.d.), "I'm not interested in whether you've stood with the great; I'm interested in whether you've sat with the broken". Contrasted with fantasies of two-martini lunches, every difficulty that I encounter this day will feel different because I feel genuinely connected to this narrative that I have chosen to sit with the broken. I have chosen purpose over easy pleasures.

Note that our antecedent narrative begins with the self-talk we engage in that defines the "short arc" of just today—opening up to this situation, this day. But the self-talk that resonates with us is filtered through, and resonates with, the "long arc"—my connection to a core belief that this work is deeply, and personally, meaningful.

Conscious Narrative: Concepts to Skills

Each of the CE-CERT skills begins with an intention. "There is no art without intention" according to Duke Ellington (Beete, 2016). And—without intention—your narrative may go places that deplete you and erode your morale. Your narrative continues to write itself all day long. The only question is whether you are the passenger or the driver of this narrative. In the next chapter, I will offer some reflections for you to consider—*really* decide—if this is the right job for you. I don't know you or your organization. This question of your job's appropriateness for you is both worthy and important. But, for the sake of this narrative skill, I'm going to stipulate that the job that you do is right for you, and that you play an important role serving people who have experienced trauma. If you *believe* that it is true that your role is an important one, but don't often think of this with a conviction that motivates you—then your narrative is driving away without you.

Your narrative contains the meaning-making about your work that you are telling continuously. It includes the evaluations you have made about yourself, the organization that you work for, and the clients you serve. It includes the meaning that you make from aversive moments, and from your stress. Most importantly, it includes the valences—positive and negative—that you place on every aspect of everything that you do each day—those valences are the editorial choices that you are constantly making. And some of those choices may be negatively affecting your stress level and your sense of wellness on the job. Our goal is to get closer to reality and to identify the distortions that we have made.

The intention with which we begin is to become more conscious of our narrative. We want to be the driver of this account and not a passenger. In CBT, this is accomplished with extensive logs of events, irrational thoughts, and rational substitutions. If you are ambitious, this is an excellent exercise for becoming aware of your narratives about your job ("I hate this job!" vs. "This is hard, but I can let myself feel this for a little while".). With or without keeping logs, begin to pay focused, deliberate attention to your self-talk before work, during rewarding and stressful moments at work, and after stressful events.

As the clinical director of a community mental health center, I became very aware of how differently various therapists felt about their days of psychotherapy. At one end of the bell curve were those who seemed to wish to avoid doing psychotherapy or spending time with clients at all, and at the other end were those for whom doing psychotherapy was like oxygen. They couldn't get enough of it. As a clinical supervisor, I wanted to know the difference. Was it personality? Did the passionately committed psychotherapists have "self-care" strategies that the burned-out therapists could learn? I conducted a formal, qualitative study to try to identify what distinguished the "passionately committed psychotherapists" and what they had in common. Although the limits of my study didn't allow me to discern physiological or personality characteristics, one factor was utterly consistent: the *narratives* of the passionately committed psychotherapists had many elements in common (Miller, 2007). I believe that career-sustaining narratives are what distinguishes the passionately committed psychotherapists from the ones who burn out.

Although there are certain narrative themes that will sustain you in your career, I can't write them here as incantations and have them transform how you experience your work. But you can cultivate them—because they are rational and fact-based. Not just "positive thinking" but reckoning the truth; either as current statements of truth or because they are aspirational and can become true. Consider the narrative themes I will propose here. Ask yourself if these statements currently exist within your narrative. Intentionally become mindful of these—or similar—narrative themes. Not as affirmations, but as a rational reflection of your actual or intended experience.

Conscious Oversight of Our Antecedent Narrative

Two priming narratives are essential: one is over the short arc of this day, and the other is the long arc of my narrative of personal meaning about my vocation. One of the central techniques in sports psychology is picturing the perfect performance before the contest: the perfect golf swing, the perfect execution of the 400-meter hurdles. That is what you are doing with your priming narrative. "I am open to the feelings that this day will bring". Or, even better (if you can allow it to be true), "I am really curious to see what experiences will come up for me today". You are imagining the perfect performance—which is to say openness to any feelings of sadness, anxiety, frustration, heart-break, as well as joy, pleasure, and deep satisfaction. You are setting an intention.

The long arc narrative of personal meaning in our work is a never-finished story. You may reflect on this narrative and even think about it when you are at a professional conference. Perhaps you reflect on it when you read a book such as this one. You are likely to employ this narrative when you are in conversation with someone about what you do for a living, especially if they indicate a curiosity about why you do this line of work. But unfortunately, we often get disconnected from this narrative. We are challenged by the daily-ness of our work. We are numbed by the sameness of our tasks. Our attention is on the next task and when we complete that, immediately moves to whatever is next. But our attention rarely goes to the *most important thing:* why I am doing this, and why I believe it matters.

As a program leader in a children's hospital, I instituted a routine to address this. Each week during clinical rounds I asked my administrative assistant to signal me when we had reviewed half of the cases on the day's agenda. Before moving to the second half, I would call out to the team for any stories of "grace and goosebumps". Stories of grace were, I explained, those moments when a clinical case took an unexpected turn for the better—better than you predicted. Stories of goosebumps were those experiences that brought you to awareness of the importance of what we were endeavoring to do.

This routine was an unequivocal success. Not only were my team members *always* able to identify stories of grace and goosebumps, they also relished the stories of their peers. And—most convincingly to me—were the times outside of clinical rounds when a therapist would say, "I've got to share a goosebump moment that just happened..." I believe that this simple exercise helped the team to notice and savor moments that would have otherwise escaped notice—and would have never become part of their narrative about "why I do this". We were doing what Kurt Vonnegut Jr. suggested; we were taking a moment to consider "if this isn't nice, I don't know what is". These moments occur frequently. But if we don't notice and savor them, they will not be part of our narrative. And that will be as if they never happened at all.

Conscious Narrative: Telling Our Story

Self-Audit

1. How often does your work remind you of your own personal mission?

Never						Weekly	Daily			
0	1	2	3	4	5	6	7	8	9	10

2. Divide the pie chart below into the proper proportions of how much of your job contains activities that produce these feelings: 1) stress/anxiety; 2) fear; 3) neutral busywork; 4) boredom; 5) pleasure/joy

3. When you anticipate coming into work on a typical day, how often do you feel emotionally open to the day's events and tasks?

Never						Weekly	Daily			
0	1	2	3	4	5	6	7	8	9	10

4. How often do you feel overwhelmed by a client or a job task that you must do?

Never						Weekly	Daily			
0	1	2	3	4	5	6	7	8	9	10

5. How would you rate the truth of this statement: "I am open to accepting the discomfort of situations that arise in my work".

Never						Sometimes	Always			
0	1	2	3	4	5	6	7	8	9	10

6. Reflect on your responses to this self-audit and what you know about yourself. Draw the needle on the experiential engagement gauge (scale = 1–10) where you would currently rate yourself:

Descriptive Statements for Gauge

Gray	• I pay attention to the story I am telling myself (and others) about my work.
	• I often think of the personal meaning I find in my work.
	• I feel that I am good at the hard parts of my job.
	• I use stress to motivate me.
	• I take time to think about what my experiences have meant to me, and to notice my professional growth.
Light Gray	• I sometimes get lost in being busy and disconnect from my sense of personal meaning.
	• Sometimes I get overwhelmed by what my job requires of me.
	• I sometimes don't feel competent at what I am doing.
Black	• I don't think what I do matters.
	• I often feel overwhelmed and that I'm not up to this job.
	• It's too demanding to take time to reflect on it all.

References

Beete, P. (February 10, 2016). *That time Duke Elliot said....* Retrieved from https://www.arts.gov/ stories/blog/2016/time-duke-ellington-said.

Bruzzese, F., Olb, J., & Parry, M. (2018). *Hannah* [Television broadcast]. HBO.

Creswell, J. D., Way, B. M., Eisenberger, N. I., & Lieberman, M. D. (2007). Neural correlates of dispositional mindfulness during affect labeling. *Psychosomatic Medicine, 69*(6), 560–565.

Fitzmaurice, S. (n.d.). *Goodreads (Website).* Retrieved from https://www.goodreads.com/quotes/8160827-i-m-not-interested-in-whether-you-ve-stood-with-the-great.

Gallo, C. (October 11, 2013). Brené Brown's presentation caught Oprah's attention. The same skills can work for you. *Forbes Magazine.* Retrieved from https://www.forbes.com/sites/carminegallo/2013/10/11/brene-browns-presentation-caught-oprahs-attention-the-same-skills-can-work-for-you/?sh=460e67ea53c1http://discovermagazine.com/.

James, W. (2013). *What is an emotion?* New York: Start Publishing LLC.

Kipling, R. (n.d.). *Words are the most powerful drug used by mankind.* Retrieved January 3, 2021, from https://www.forbes.com/quotes/8260/.

La Guin, U. (2014). Another story of a fisherman of the Island Sea. In A. Vandermeer & J. Vandermeer (Eds.), *The time traveler's almanac*. New York: Tor Books.

Maharaj, S. N. (2017). *Desire and fear are based on memories*. Retrieved from http://srinisargadattamaharaj.com/nisargadatta-teachings/desire-and-fear-are-based-on-memories/.

Miller, B. (2007). Innovations: Psychotherapy: What creates and sustains commitment to the practice of psychotherapy?. *Psychiatric Services, 58*(2), 174–176.

Rukeyser, M. (n.d.) *The speed of darkness*. Poem. Retrieved January 3, 2021, from https://www.poetryfoundation.org/poems/56287/the-speed-of-darkness.

Siegel, D. J. (2007). *The mindful brain: Reflection and attunement in the cultivation of well-being (Norton series on interpersonal neurobiology)*. New York: WW Norton and Company.

Torrisi, S. J., Lieberman, M. D., Bookheimer, S. Y., & Altshuler, L. L. (2013). Advancing understanding of affect labeling with dynamic causal modeling. *NeuroImage, 82*, 481–488.

Zhang, W., van Ast, V. A., Klumpers, F., Roelofs, K., & Hermans, E. J. (2018). Memory contextualization: The role of prefrontal cortex in functional integration across item and context representational regions. *Journal of Cognitive Neuroscience, 30*(4), 579–593.

5 Point of Contact: The Concurrent Narrative

Conscious Narrative: Telling Our Story

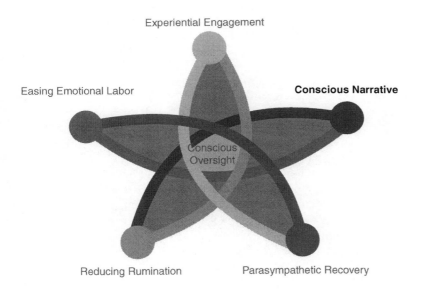

Experiential Engagement

Easing Emotional Labor

Conscious Narrative

Conscious Oversight

Reducing Rumination

Parasympathetic Recovery

> The greatest weapon against stress is our ability to choose one thought over another.
>
> William James (2013)

Introduction

And now we arrive at the second act. In the classic three-act story, the second act is the moment of engagement; this is when we begin the quest. The concurrent narrative is the running dialogue *during* the challenge—during stress events. What you tell yourself when you are squarely in the moment will not only determine how you feel about the situation, it will determine the physiological response that you experience during and after the stress event.

A few years ago, I directed a trauma program at a mental health center serving preschool-age children. Because my role was administrative, a couple of times a week I practiced a routine to help ground me in the reality of the mission of the agency. At 9:00 AM the preschoolers would assemble in the waiting area as the van drivers and parents brought them in until eventually the area was filled with four-year-olds. My routine was to take a deep mindful breath, become aware of my feet beneath me, and mindfully notice the faces of the four-year-old children at that age of perfect cuteness. "You", I could chant to myself, "are why I do this". This grounding exercise was my way of connecting with my sense of meaning in my job.

One day as I did this mindfulness exercise, I glanced upon a little boy I hadn't seen before. He could have been an advertisement for Frosted Flakes, or some other product marketed to kids—unusually cute, even for a four-year-old. When he was presented by his social worker/therapist at our admissions meeting that morning, I learned that just a few weeks prior he had been physically abused by his mother to a degree that he nearly lost his life. I was emotionally overcome that this could have happened to this little boy, who betrayed none of that history in his open demeanor or appearance.

Now imagine for a moment that you are this four-year-old boy's therapist. Sitting across from you is this perfect little human who has—though he is as innocent as he looks—suffered horrible abuse. And now you have the responsibility to attempt to repair as much of that damage as possible. Let me illustrate two different concurrent narratives that you might employ. The first one is this: "He is so unbelievably innocent and vulnerable. I just can't accept that this world would allow someone as innocent as him to suffer that way. I don't even know if I want to live in such a world. And how do I fix this? I can't undo what happened. His foster parents are looking at me wanting to know what to do. His reactive behaviors are so complex, I don't know where to begin..."

This narrative—which could be summarized as "I am overwhelmed by the sadness and complexity of this case..." will have very specific psychological and physiological outcomes. This has become a stress event, so my sympathetic system is activated. Because my narrative is "I am overwhelmed...", the amygdala is toned, and the flight system is activated to seek relief from this sense of distress. This is likely to lead to avoidance of some kind—perhaps dampening down my overall feeling for this situation or this little boy, or even perhaps requesting that the case be transferred. This narrative—these words—translate into very real physiological sequelae and very real behavioral responses.

Now envision another narrative. In fact, his therapist was seasoned enough that she had experienced a number of similar situations, and similar children. Her narrative sounded more like this: "I have seen similar situations before. I know what to do—for the foster parents and for this boy. If I do my job well, I have a chance to change the trajectory of this very young child's entire life. The first thing to do is to engage with him and his new foster parents and I do that by..."

This narrative—that could be summarized as "I know what to do here..." will result in a very different psychological and physiological response in this therapist. Thinking about this case in a problem-solving fashion activates the pre-frontal cortex. Activity in the pre-frontal cortex activates parasympathetic recovery, resulting in a physical and psychological calming of the therapist. The possibility of potentially resolving some of this child's suffering and putting him on a path of recovery is stimulating—it results in eustress, the positive form of the stress response. This results in a sense of emotionally opening to the child, curiosity about the complexities of this case, and allows for full engagement.

The same child and set of circumstances could, in a very material way, have such a differential effect upon two therapists. The determining factor is the *concurrent narrative* that the therapists employ. "I am overwhelmed..." versus "I know what to do here...".

Because many of us have a sense of chronic stress in our work, we naturally have a desire for things to slow down, become less intense, to get easier. We maintain the fantasy of going to that tropical island and getting away from it all. That is why it is worth remembering that our engagement and enjoyment of our work occurs when the demands of the job are highest. We are in "the zone" not when we are in a demand-less state, but when we are focused on something challenging—but within our skill level. The fantasy of being totally without stress really isn't desirable because of the demands of the job—it is, rather, because of two narratives about the demands: A perceived mismatch between the demands of our job and our sense of our capability, and the resulting feeling of being overwhelmed by it all. Narratives of mastery inoculate us from this form of stress. Mastery of the job's craft of knowing how to intervene in the case, but also a sense of mastery of our ability to manage our own emotions.

The tropical paradise fantasy results from the narrative that ease is the goal. This relates, again, to our willingness narrative. Are we willing to experience difficult situations and difficult emotions, or is our narrative some version of "I just want this to be easier" or "I just want to get away from this"?

What if, instead of the desire for this to become easy, we cultivated a narrative of "I am willing to experience this difficult situation (feeling)"? Imagine yourself tasting Scandinavian salted licorice for the first time. "*It is supposed to be* intense and salty". Maybe if you open up to it you will like it. Maybe you'll hate it. Liking it isn't the necessary condition. The necessary narrative is "I am willing to experience this". As the psychiatrist Theodore Isaac Rubin said, "the problem is not that there are problems. The problem is expecting otherwise and thinking that having problems is a problem" (Rubin, 1993).

An important element of the concurrent narrative concerns the self-talk that you employ during the stress event. When under stress, you are labeling and describing the stress to yourself—your stress narrative. Kelly McGonigal gave a widely viewed TED talk in which she described research conducted by Keller et al. (2012). These researchers linked data from the 1998 National Health Interview Survey and the National Death Index mortality data through 2006. This data allowed them to examine how much stress people reported that they were under as well as their perceptions of that stress. The researchers reviewed who died over the term of the study. Then, all subjects' responses to two questions were tallied: 1) How would you rate the amount of stress you have been under the past year? and 2) Do you believe that stress has impacted your health? Death records were checked to see how many of the individuals who responded to the health interview had died.

It is surprising to see who was healthiest, and who did worst, based on their responses. The first surprise is that those who reported that they were under low levels of stress the past year *did not have lower rates of mortality.* Nor did they do the worst. Surprise number two is who were most likely to die over the term of the data: those who responded that they had *high levels of stress* and *that the stress had affected their health* were significantly more likely to have died during the study period. They, obviously, were correct—apparently stress had affected their health.

And finally, and most usefully, was the category that was least likely to appear on the mortality report: those who responded that they were under *high levels of stress*, but who didn't believe that the stress had a negative effect upon their health.

This finding raises an intriguing prospect: stress itself isn't inherently harmful to our health. But what we tell ourselves about our stress—our stress narrative—can make all the difference. We have long known that some forms of stress—eustress—are healthy. This study demonstrates empirically that different cognitive and physiological processes are activated based on the particular narrative that we employ during a stress event, rendering it as eustress or distress.

Other research demonstrates that not only does our stress narrative influence our health, but it also profoundly affects our job performance. Brooks did an interesting study in which she asked college students to deliver a persuasive speech with only two minutes to prepare. Their speeches were going to be video recorded and evaluated by a team of judges. This study was designed to cause stress in the subjects. The independent variable in the study is whether the subjects were told to say to themselves "I am calm" or "I am excited" (in Grant & Sandberg, 2016). The results were fascinating: those who labeled their stress as "excitement" performed better in ratings of confidence and persuasiveness and how long they remained at the podium. They outperformed those who—in contradiction to what their body was telling them—maintained the narrative "I am calm".

Consider the profundity in this simple experiment—simply changing one word—from calm to excited—determines how you will tolerate the stress. This finding has been replicated in multiple ways in multiple studies. The world really is made of stories—and your stress response certainly is made of your narrative.

Stress is not an emotion. It is the physiological response to any number of emotions. These emotions might be anger, fear, or frustration. The Latin root of emotion, *emovere*, refers to motion. The combination of feelings that we label "stress" are motivating us to move. The direction of our movement—physical or emotional—will be determined by how we label our stress experience. In Brooks' experiment, half of the subjects were told to label that as "excitement". That leads to a narrative: "this feeling of my heart pounding and shortness of breath is because I am excited; my excitement will help me focus on this task..." That narrative conveys a *toward* energy that moves us into the fray (problem solving and contending with the stressor).

The other half of the subjects were coached to say, "I'm calm", but clearly, their body knew better. This label did not lead to a narrative of "I am calm because I am confident that I will give a great persuasive speech". Considerable research has demonstrated the power of *accurately* labeling emotions. But this study was an example of how mislabeling our emotions doesn't work. Our body knows we are experiencing stress, and our label must accurately account for our internal reactions. Saying "I am calm..." when they were not had a paradoxical effect: it primed a narrative of "No, I'm not calm. I'm freaking out!" And that "real narrative" also became fact, as measured by poorer performance and briefer speeches.

The central thesis of this chapter is that intense experiences demand a narrative. If I label my stress reactions as preparing me to deal with an intense experience, my stress will do exactly that. I will think faster, recall better, and engage more fully *because* of the stress. This excitement narrative activates the pre-frontal cortex/eustress/engagement pathway. Eustress is the health and performance promoting form of stress. Labeling our stress as energizing us to contend with a situation doesn't mean it will feel good. Again, it is ineffective to mislabel our stress. But this positive label does allow us to direct our energy into contending with the situation—being focused on solving the problem rather than emotional soothing.

If, however, I label my stress as something that is bad for me and intolerable, the direction of my motion will be *away* from the stressor and toward emotion-focused coping. My energies will go toward suppressing my emotions and trying to tamp down my stress. I will use a lot of energy this way, but it will be "away" energy, trying to get away from the situation or my emotions. This is distress. This activates the amygdala/distress/relief-seeking pathway. I put the brakes on so that I don't literally run away, but my emotions are still at full throttle. I am in full fight or flight but am trying to calm my feelings. As a result, I probably feel a little more helpless—the very helplessness that we are working to dispel with the CE-CERT skills repertoire.

Another factor that will influence long-term wellness in your role as a trauma therapist is specific to the narrative about situations that are simply beyond therapeutic repair. My experience is that physicians and psychotherapists love to assess, diagnose, and formulate interventions. We love our "tool kits", and we are energized by our ability to use those tools. But what about those situations that simply cannot be fixed? What if this client has an illness that is certain to result in their death? What if this child's caregivers are so broken that they are unable to offer this child what she needs and are unwilling to accept your help? What if this client, in spite of your most ambitious efforts, is simply not getting well? In these situations—when our usual diagnose-it-and-fix-it strategy fails us, we don't know what to do. And when we are feeling helpless is when secondary trauma occurs.

There is an important fact—not just nicety, but fact—that can be cultivated in your narrative about inevitable suffering. That fact is this: "I still can be of support to this person even though I cannot alleviate their pain". This narrative will sustain you. What is your personal narrative when you encounter tragic but immutable situations with your clients? Almost certainly, your narrative is implicit rather than verbalized. But when you state it explicitly, its irrationality becomes apparent: "I must know how to fix any form of suffering that my client experiences". And if this irrational narrative isn't corrected, it is easy to see how exhausting—and how disheartening—this impossible goal will be as we strain toward it.

Perhaps your implicit narrative isn't so comprehensive. Perhaps, if it were to be verbalized, it would be closer to this: "If I can't remedy this circumstance for this person, then I don't know what I *can* do". I believe that many therapists maintain this unstated belief, and that this narrative exhausts them in the helping role. Because they can't fix the unfixable, they don't know what to target with their therapeutic skills.

When your client is dealing with an unfortunate but unchangeable circumstance, you must give up your struggle to find the "word magic" that will fix this situation. You are not a witch doctor, and you cannot conjure anything that will change what is. There is one thing—and only one thing—that you can do, however. You can remain emotionally present and empathically attuned to your client. You can express and demonstrate that you will empathize with this difficult reality. And this isn't doing nothing. It matters. It may mean everything to this person.

And finally, it is important that I emphasize that our concurrent narrative isn't only about stress events. We also maintain an active, continuous narrative about the pleasant and rewarding experiences that we are having each day. Our brain selectively emphasizes the danger and the stress-producing—fortunate for survival in the evolutionary sense, but unfortunate for job enjoyment. We must actively cultivate the ability to notice and savor the positive. As Kurt Vonnegut Jr. said pithily in his book *A Man Without a Country*, "And I urge you to please notice when you are happy, and exclaim or murmur or think at some point, 'If this isn't nice, I don't know what is'" (Vonnegut & Simon, 2005).

We have to notice these moments with deliberateness. However stressful your job is, these moments are plentiful. They are the big moments that connect us to, "Yes, this is why I wanted to do this job". And they are the little moments, small simple pleasures like laughing because our young patient said something funny. We get so busy that we miss them because we have trained our attention toward what needs to be done now, or upon anticipation of the next stressor on the horizon.

Here is an important self-reflection: when was the last time you had an experience in your work that led you to say to yourself, "Oh yes, this is why I wanted to do this for a living"? If it has been a long time, then—as an auto mechanic might say, "There's your problem, Ma'am". If it is rare for you to have those moments—and to entertain that narrative—this is a rich area to target in the cultivation of your conscious narrative.

Bridging Concepts to Skills

Conscious Oversight of the Concurrent Narrative

What do you say to yourself in the midst of "fighting the dragon"? In the very midst of the stress event, what are you telling yourself about the situation and about your feelings? Are you telling yourself that you expected tough moments like this or that this is an unexpected and unwelcome surprise?

Consider how much of your stress derives from encountering situations where you don't know what to do or where to begin. Often, tasks that we find aversive are so because we have to work so hard to get through them. Consider the clear differential effect a narrative of "I am totally lost here...", compared to a narrative of "I know exactly what to do here". Perhaps you really are totally lost. What is your concurrent narrative about that? Is it "I need to develop more knowledge/skill about this" or is it "I can't stand this feeling of not knowing what to do"?

I had a profound teachable moment as a young psychotherapist. I was being totally transparent and, I think, offering a moment of grace when I said to a patient, "Wow. This is really hard. I don't even know what to say here, or what to suggest. I'm thinking maybe I'm feeling right now the way you feel a lot of the time..." This acknowledgment was experienced as very validating by my patient. I would even say it marked a new level in my relationship with her. And—with her and all my subsequent patients—it got so much easier because I knew that I could acknowledge my limits anytime I needed to. I gave up the unattainable narrative: "I always must have a brilliant insight into my client's problem".

A second element of a career-sustaining narrative relates to experiential engagement. This narrative is a narrative that allows us to open our willingness: "I am willing to experience this..." In the midst of an unpleasant or stressful task, we open to it. It is important that our self-talk incorporates the truth—this may be unpleasant, but it is tolerable. And it is time limited—usually only a few moments. "I know that there will be problems, and some of them are difficult. I am willing to feel stuck, frustrated, and even stressed".

The third skill for building a concurrent narrative—part of our stress narrative—enhances our hardiness in the job. A recurring concept in CE-CERT is that a healthy response to stressors requires the twin skills of being able to turn on the stress response when the environment demands, and to turn it off after the stress event has ended. Stress is not always a bad or unhealthy thing. But stress doesn't feel good. When we are breathing fast and feeling pressure, when our heart is pounding, it often is uncomfortable. But the way we explain those physiological effects to ourselves makes all the difference. We want our stress narrative to be one that allows the stress as a healthy response (willingness) even if it is uncomfortable, and we want our narrative to put our stress to work (provide a "toward energy"). A healthy stress narrative might sound something like this: "This feeling of discomfort is me getting ready to contend with this situation. It will help me make decisions faster and engage more fully. I will recover after this is taken care of".

And fourth, a sustaining concurrent narrative explains our role in situations that are unfortunate, but immutable. Developing an equanimity-based narrative requires first that we recognize those unchangeable circumstances when we encounter them, so we don't wear ourselves out in the fruitless attempt to find the right tool. "I can't repair everything in this client's world. And they may need my support in radically accepting this reality". "I can't fix this. But I'm willing to remain present for the person who is suffering". "I can't make this go away for him/her. But I know how to express my empathy for them—and that is important".

The narrative of our work, of course, must not only be based on hardship and suffering. One of the editorial choices we must make is a robust focus on the rewards and positive experiences that we encounter each day. We need to create opportunities to step out of the "daily-ness" of our work to notice and savor the pleasurable and rewarding events that happen to us nearly every day. They are happening all around us in this work helping people recover from trauma. We must notice them and make them a central element of our narrative. If we succeed, this narrative can sustain us for a very long and rewarding career.

Point of Contact: The Concurrent Narrative

Self-Audit

1. I am willing to emotionally stay with a person who is dealing with a situation that cannot be changed without trying to advise or fix.

Never					Sometimes	Always				
0	1	2	3	4	5	6	7	8	9	10

2. Stress motivates me to engage a difficult client situation (as opposed to trying to move away).

Never					Sometimes	Always				
0	1	2	3	4	5	6	7	8	9	10

3. Reflect on your responses to this self-audit and what you know about yourself. Draw the needle on the experiential engagement gauge (scale = 1–10) where you would currently rate yourself:

Descriptive Statements for Gauge

Gray	• I continue to know what my role is when I can't fix my client's circumstances • I feel that I am good at the hard parts of my job. • I use stress to motivate me. • When a situation is unpleasant and intense, I am telling myself that I am willing to be uncomfortable
Light Gray	• I sometimes get lost in being busy and disconnect from my sense of personal meaning. • Sometimes I get overwhelmed by what my job requires of me. • I sometimes don't feel competent at what I am doing.
Black	• I often feel overwhelmed and that I'm not up to this job. • I feel like stress is killing me.

References

Grant, A. M., & Sandberg, S. (2016). *Originals: How non-conformists move the world*. New York, New York: Viking.

James, W. (2013). *What is an emotion?* New York: Start Publishing LLC.

Keller, A., Litzelman, K., Wisk, L. E., Maddox, T., Cheng, E. R., Creswell, P. D., & Witt, W. P. (2012). Does the perception that stress affects health matter? The association with health and mortality. *Health Psychology, 31*(5), 677.

Rubin, T. I. (1993). *The angry book*. New York: Simon & Schuster.

Vonnegut, K., & Simon, D. (2005). *A man without a country*. New York: Seven Stories Press.

6 Stories Around the Fire: The Consolidation Narrative

Conscious Narrative: Telling Our Story

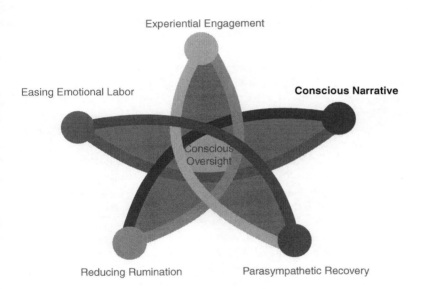

And He [The Angel] said, "Let Me go, for the day breaks." But he said, "I will not let You go unless You bless me!"

Genesis 32:26 New King James Version[1]

The Consolidation Narrative

Perhaps you know the biblical story of Jacob wrestling the angel. In that telling, Jacob struggles with an angel through the night. At one point, the angel touches Jacob's hip, which dislocates it from its socket. As day-break occurs, Jacob has prevailed against the angel. The angel then pleads with Jacob to release him, but Jacob refuses. He tells the angel,

"I will not release you unless you bless me". There are many varying interpretations of this story, but one interpretation adds to our discussion of the consolidation narrative. Intense experience demands a narrative—and the blessing of the struggle can be the narrative that results. Blessing in the form of what we value, or what we now know because of that experience. "I will not release you until you have blessed me..." But failing to tell the story—or telling the story improperly—can rob the event of its meaning. Then, instead of being blessed by the experience, we lose confidence, feel more helpless, or want to give up our mission. And that, of course, is why we must take care to tell the story properly. "...All sorrows can be borne", according to Dinesen (2012), "...if you put them into a story".

The consolidation narrative evokes a scene for me. It is the moment in which we are sitting around the fire with our tribe, recounting the adventures of the day. We can picture this cinematically, but this story can also be told through neurophysiology. This recalling and telling consolidates events into contextualized experience. The act of remembering and retelling requires the construction of new meaning—I summon the images, then I ascribe meaning to what happened. I make editorial choices. This is when stress memories become contextualized in our cerebral cortex rather than being fleeting, disconnected images produced by our hippocampus. Contextualization by the pre-frontal cortex is what distinguishes consolidated memories from post-traumatic intrusive thoughts. It is putting it all in context that makes the memories useful instead of intrusive (Liberzon & Abelson, 2016; Zhang et al., 2018).

Forming a narrative after an experience is when we make sense of what has taken place. As Margaret Atwood says in her novel *Alias Grace*, "When you are in the middle of a story it isn't a story at all, but only a confusion; a dark roaring, a blindness, a wreckage of shattered glass and splintered wood; like a house in a whirlwind, or else a boat crushed by the icebergs or swept over the rapids, and all aboard powerless to stop it. It's only afterwards that it becomes anything like a story at all. When you are telling it, to yourself or to someone else" (1997).

In creative writing classes, memoir is sometimes defined as "what 'what happened' means". In the midst of the moment, we can only be aware of what is happening. It is in the consolidation that we can discern—and can shape—what 'what happened' means to us—and what we will do with 'what happened" means.

In the psychotherapeutic professions we are fortunate to have a tradition of clinical supervision dating back to the origins of psychoanalysis. Most occupations—including medicine—do not have this benefit. Clinical supervision is an opportunity already baked into our routines to allow us to form a consolidation narrative. Although it may be a novel way to describe it, narrative formation is the chief objective of a supervision session. Supervision includes processing these difficult events so that we can put them into a context that helps us resolve difficult situations. This how we increase our professional proficiency.

Of course, most of our consolidation narratives were not formulated during clinical supervision. Narrative formation happens organically through the day. For me—and probably for most of us—the best supervision I ever received was in the form of "hallway consults" with peers. These consults were often discussions of how to approach difficult cases and reviews of challenging or upsetting cases. Staff meetings also often serve this purpose, if only in the form of sidebar conversations. And even more often, we have moments of reflection in the solitude of our own office. So, we have opportunities—even in busy workplaces—for reflection and narrative formation. Our new task, then, is to consciously direct these narratives in ways that will sustain us.

Extending William James (2013), I would suggest that "the greatest weapon we have against job stress is our ability to choose one narrative over another". I don't find that to be too "heaven minded"—It is as empirical as is CBT. We can choose a narrative that depletes our morale and motivation, "I'm not getting anywhere with her. This is a waste of my time"; or we can choose narratives that kindle our motivation, "I haven't found a way in yet. I think maybe I've been too task-focused with her. Maybe I need to find a way to make her feel understood..."

The legendary civil rights activist Ruby Sales defines the complete self as possessing foresight, insight, and hindsight (Jones et al., 2007). Each of these attributes relate to the three acts of the narrative: before, during, and after. But these are also the elements of an effective consolidation narrative. *Insight:* "What lessons can be gleaned from this event?" "I will not release you until you have blessed me..." *Hindsight:* "When I look at how I did in this circumstance, what did I do right, and what could I have done better?" *Foresight:* What will I do next time I encounter a similar circumstance?"

In the classic story structure, the consolidation narrative completes the third act. It is the denouement, the resolution. And we need this third act in very real, practical terms—we need to mark the end of the stress event. We need to know that I am here, reflecting about the lessons of this event, and the stress is there, in the past. Then—and only then—will the parasympathetic nervous system hit the off switch to our stress. This is when the shipwreck becomes a contextualized memory. I am back, safe in my cabin. The bear is not here in this time or this place...

Bridging Concepts to Skills

Conscious Oversight of the Consolidation Narrative

The first step in establishing a consolidation narrative is to assure that there is, in fact, a consolidation narrative at all. In other words, assuring that we create the space to reflect about the effect that difficult experiences had upon us. In order to tell our story properly, we must make sure that we have told the "third act" of the narrative. Looking back on that situation, what happened exactly? Maybe it looks different with the benefit of hindsight. I will see my own reactions differently when I'm not in the shipwreck of the moment. I will see my client's behaviors differently from a distance. Now I can put it all in context. This context will make any similar experiences in the future easier. And the story can end when the third act has been told.

The two essential consolidation narratives that will sustain us are: 1) our competency in the job is advancing, and 2) there was meaning in unpleasant experiences. "I learned this from the experience (about myself, about my client, about how to contend with these situations)". "This is what I did right…This is what I did wrong…This is what I will do next time…" In the Southern US, there is a saying that "everyone you meet is either a blessin' or a lesson". Every client success is a learning experience—and nearly every therapist will agree that they learned the most from the most difficult clients, even if at the time they believed that they had "failed" with them.

The second essential component of a consolidation narrative is the meaning that we make from the experience. Now that I have released the angel with whom I struggled; this is how they have blessed me. It may be that, because of the struggle to succeed with a very difficult client, they became your teacher. It may be that through the success you observed, you are more convinced that what you do matters. Or it may even be the hard lesson that the best we can do in some circumstances is to accept our own limits.

The existence of the consolidation narrative transforms random suffering into meaning. "She was the worst client I ever worked with…" becomes "That was very hard—I learned so much". That narrative can make the difference between "I hate my job…" and "I am becoming more skillful. I know now how to better intervene with my clients, and how to take emotional care of myself".

Some of you already journal. Perhaps journaling is on your list of things-I'm-going-to-start-doing-someday. I strongly promote journaling. Your journal is your written consolidation narrative. This is your time to reflect about your experiences and their effect upon you. Many people benefit more from written narratives and are better able to reflect when they write. Consider if this is true for you.

Judith Herman, in her classic text *Trauma and Recovery*, said, "Folk wisdom is filled with stories of ghosts who refuse to be buried until their story is told" (1997). And so it is with our stressful experiences—the little ones, as well as signal events. As both psychological and physiological events, we cannot fully resolve them—bury those ghosts—until we have formulated them into our narrative. And then, in context, the ghosts of the stress of those experiences are transformed into our ancestors—lessons we will know how to use. The angel has blessed us. Now we can release him…

Conscious Narrative: Cultivating the Three Acts of Our Job Story

You Must Remember This

- *Intense experiences demand a narrative.* Our brain has evolved to create narratives, because narratives are necessary to resolve the stress response. Fight or flight resolves when we convert the experience into a contextualized narrative.
- A coherent narrative consists of

   - The *antecedent* narrative: Prepares us for stress events before they occur
   - The *concurrent* narrative: The self-talk we engage in during a stress event and over the course of the day
   - The *consolidation* narrative: How we make sense of the events (both positive and negative) after they are over

- A "story" is a simple telling of the facts of the event. A "narrative" includes the choices we make about the story—what we emphasize, what valences we place on different elements, and what we leave in and what we leave out. We can't change the story—but we have great cognitive freedom over the narrative.

Bridging Concepts to Skills

1. Setting an Intention: A "conscious narrative" is one of which we are continuously aware and one that we are deliberately cultivating. Developing a conscious narrative begins with *setting an intention to*:

   a. Focus deliberate attention upon the narrative you are telling yourself. Become conscious of the narration that you are doing before, during, and after your workday.
   b. Cultivate narratives that are both accurate and career-sustaining. Deliberately take issue with narratives that erode your energy and job satisfaction (but aren't based in fact).

2. Antecedent Narrative: Cultivate narratives that

   a. Prime openness to experience, "I am open to feel all that happens today..."
   b. Connect us to a sense of the personal meaning in our work

3. Concurrent Narrative: Rehearse narratives that

   a. Provide a sense of mastery over the stress event, "I know just what to do here..."

b. Open us to experience, "I am willing to allow this uncomfortable feeling..."
c. Interpret the stress response as motivation toward action, "This stress is preparing me to deal with this..."
d. Maintain equanimity when dealing with circumstances that cannot be fixed, "I can't take away this person's suffering, but I can remain emotionally present for them..."
e. Maintain our connectedness to our sense of meaning, "Yes, this is why I do this work..."

4. Consolidation Narrative: Assure that you hold space for opportunities to reflect on events that have affected you positively or negatively. Narratives that are sustaining are those which:

a. Create a continuous narrative of advancing competency in our work, and an increasing sense of personal accomplishment
b. Help us define the meaning of profound events

The Consolidation Narrative

Self-Audit

1. After an intense situation at work, I take time to reflect on what happened and consider what meaning can be taken from the situation.

Never					Sometimes				Always	
0	1	2	3	4	5	6	7	8	9	10

2. I am finding that situations that used to be very difficult are becoming easier.

Never					Some Situations				Always	
0	1	2	3	4	5	6	7	8	9	10

3. I am finding that situations that are stressful and unpleasant are as meaningful (or more) than pleasant experiences.

Never					Some Situations				Always
0	1	2	3	4	5	6	7	8	9	10

4. Reflect on your responses to this self-audit, and what you know about yourself. Draw the needle on the experiential

engagement gauge (scale = 1–10) where you would currently rate yourself:

Descriptive Statements for Gauge

Green	• I take time to think about what my experiences have meant to me, and to notice my professional growth. • I feel like I have learned the most from the most difficult clients. • I value supervision, either with peers or formal supervisors
Yellow-into-orange	• I sometimes get lost in being busy and disconnect from my sense of personal meaning. • I sometimes get too busy to reflect on the narrative of my work. • It's a toss-up: Sometimes, I'm telling my story and sometimes my story is writing itself.
Red	• I don't think what I do matters. • It's too demanding to take time to reflect on it all.

Note

1 Scripture taken from the New King James Version®. Copyright © 1982 by Thomas Nelson. Used by permission. All rights reserved.

References

Atwood, M. (1997). *Alias Grace*. Boston: G.K. Hall.

Dinesen, I. (June 2, 2012). *Quotes by Isak Dinesen on life and storytelling.* Retrieved January 3, 2021, from https://www.literaryladiesguide.com/author-quotes/isak-dinesen-quotes/.

Herman, J. L. (1997). *Trauma and recovery*. New York: BasicBooks.

James, W. (2013). *What is an emotion?* New York: Start Publishing LLC.

Jones, C., Harvey, A. G., & Brewin, C. R. (2007). The organisation and content of trauma memories in survivors of road traffic accidents. *Behaviour Research and Therapy*, *45*(1), 151–162.

Liberzon, I., & Abelson, J. L. (2016). Context processing and the neurobiology of post-traumatic stress disorder. *Neuron*, *92*(1), 14–30.

Zhang, W., van Ast, V. A., Klumpers, F., Roelofs, K., & Hermans, E. J. (2018). Memory contextualization: The role of prefrontal cortex in functional integration across item and context representation regions. *Journal of Cognitive Neuroscience*, *30*(4), 579–593.

Section III
Returning with the Elixir

7   Making the Work Easier: Reducing Emotional Labor

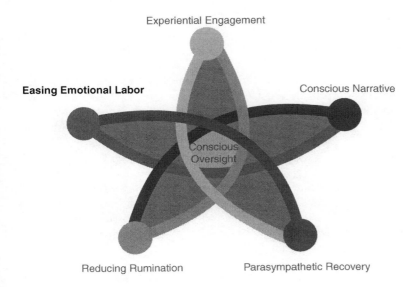

Experiential Engagement

Easing Emotional Labor

Conscious Narrative

Conscious Oversight

Reducing Rumination

Parasympathetic Recovery

Sit down and have a cup of coffee. It's already been saucered and blowed.
Invitation of Southern Hospitality

Introduction

It is a pleasure to arrive at this point in our story. Even as I write this, I feel myself beginning to relax. The third act of the classic story begins when the hero has been resurrected and purified. After succeeding in her quest, she now has returned to the ordinary world. The struggle is over. Now is the time to rest and to begin healing herself and the world. The hero brings with her the elixir that she claimed on her journey. In folklore, the elixir is a great treasure or a magic potion. But it also is sometimes a special wisdom.

I am happy to get to this part of our story because the skills discussed heretofore have felt like work: how to increase your willingness to experience difficult emotions, how to reduce ruminative thoughts, and how to direct your narratives. But now it gets easier. I saw Cornelius Talbot quoted on a greeting card: "I am tired of acquiring wisdom. Somebody, bring me a drink and a whoopie cushion".

In fact, this chapter is about how, exactly, to allow it become easier—and to understand what we are doing that is making our work harder than it must be. The central premise of this chapter is that your job will only be sustainable if it does get easier. I won't try to convince you that there is magic here, but it certainly is a kind of special wisdom. I have known many in the therapy fields that have this "elixir"—this wisdom. I believe we can benefit and learn from what is for them, perhaps, a native wisdom. But if it comes naturally for them, we also can experience this kind of ease with deliberate intent and practice.

Therapists who thrive in their work are doing so for the simplest of reasons: they love their jobs (Clark, 2009; Melamed et al., 2001; Miller, 2007). Perhaps—especially because I provided citations—you find this fact intriguing. Or maybe it seems like the most trite, self-evident statement you could imagine: the best way to thrive in your job is to enjoy your job. But this statement is deceptively profound. Of course, there is a whole lot of obviousness to the observation that we must enjoy our jobs to thrive in our jobs. *But this simple fact has been missing from our research and our discussions about professional burnout and secondary traumatic stress.* We have studied the factors and symptoms that correlate with secondary traumatic stress. We prescribe self-care activities and work–life balance to help us recover from job stress and trauma exposure. But we don't talk about making the work itself more enjoyable and less effortful.

Another bit of colorful Southern advice: "Don't be going around your ass just to get to your elbow". Maybe we are doing this the hard way—focusing on all the elements that make the work hard but losing sight of how to make it easier. This chapter isn't about trying harder; rather, it is a study of what makes work feel easier and more enjoyable.

It is common for the officials opening professional conferences to thank you for the difficult work that you do. Your supervisor also may express an appreciation for the difficulties that your work as a trauma therapist entails. There's a pretty good chance that, if I asked you, you also would say that you have a hard job.

I'm going to be a contrarian—but call this evidence-based contrarianism. Your work is, without a doubt, sometimes difficult. But here is where I think the evidence departs from the well-intended statements about how difficult your work is: those who are thriving in our field don't find it to be onerous or difficult. They enjoy their work.

It's not too early in this discussion for a quick self-audit. When someone tells you how difficult your work must be, what is your inner dialogue? Is it, "Yes, it sure is"? Or do you say to yourself, "I appreciate their recognition, but my job is pretty awesome"? It is okay to be starting from the first position—that your job sure is hard. But ultimately, we want to bring you to the second conclusion—that your job is pretty awesome.

When I conducted a formal study of passionately committed psychotherapists, I found one data point that had been hiding in plain sight.

Because researchers and trainers have been focused on measuring burnout and its sequela, we have missed something obvious. One of the queries on my interview protocol was "What strategies have you employed that have helped you maintain your energy for this work?" For the passionately committed therapists that I was interviewing, their answers were universally variations of "What strategies have I employed? ... I don't know if this is a strategy, but I just love what I do".

At first, I was disappointed to hear these passionate therapists' responses. I wanted to come away from this research project with strategies that therapists can use to bolster their energy for their work. But as I sat with this finding, I realized something useful was residing in this obvious-once-we-think-about-it fact. Here's what those passionate therapists *didn't* say: none of them said "self-care". And, interestingly, when they mentioned "work–life balance" (a topic we will discuss in the next chapter), it was not in the context of how work had crowded out the pleasurable pursuits. Instead, they talked about how they found work so compelling they had to make themselves stop in order to fit the other things in. This changed the research question. Instead of investigating recovery-from-work strategies, I realized that I was investigating work-enjoyment strategies.

The recovery-from-work narrative is based on a metaphor of a battery. The battery narrative is that your energy and enthusiasm for your work depends upon charging your battery in the evenings and weekends— because that is the energy that you operate on through the week. And—extending the metaphor further—it is as if you are driving an electric car and have to make certain that your battery will get you all the way to your destination, which is Friday at quitting time.

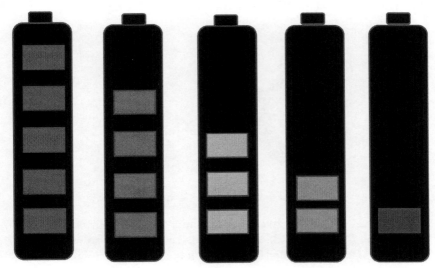

Perhaps the first, fully charged battery represents you when you were fresh out of training. You were full of energy and idealism and ready to go change the world. But—according to the battery metaphor—each year your battery gets a little more depleted. Or, maybe in your battery narrative, the first battery simply represents Monday, the second battery is Tuesday, and the last one represents Friday. By the end of the week you are fully drained and must recharge. That is the battery metaphor, and it is the implicit framework upon which the self-care, recovery-from-work advice is based.

This metaphor is the wrong narrative. Wrong because it is unhelpful. And wrong because that image isn't based in the reality of your job energy dynamic. In reality, *some* of the activities that you are engaged in are depleting. *Some* of your job tasks are stressful, and *some* of your job tasks are boring. But—since we are trying to ground our narratives in a clearer sense of reality—this battery depletion metaphor is distorting the whole truth. Because some of what you do is energizing. And some of what happens to you during your workday is stimulating and rewarding.

Ben-Shahar (2007) notes the paradox "...that we say we prefer leisure at the same time that we are having our peak experiences at work—is strange and revealing. It suggests that our prejudice against work, our association of effort with pain and leisure with pleasure, is so deep-rooted that it distorts our perception of the actual experience".

I want you to challenge the battery narrative and replace it with a more reality-based assessment of your job. In the real world, energy operates in an open energy system in which energy is being exchanged. The metaphor could be represented like this—instead of a discharging battery, there is interaction between energy creation and energy expended:

Energy Expended

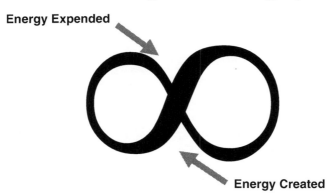

Energy Created

This model of job energy includes an important element that the battery metaphor misses: work doesn't only deplete us; it also energizes us (at times). Central to this metaphor is the infinite transactional relationship between energy expense and energy creation. Conceptually, if those two are in balance, we could sustain high energy over our entire career. It is a matter of assuring that these two dynamics are at net zero, or even on the positive side.

Viewing our job energy this way isn't just conceptual. Exactly this energy dynamic is embodied by those passionately committed therapists whom I studied—and who work with and around you (maybe it is you.) The energy that these individuals derive from work often exceeds the energy demands. As long as that is true, these therapists can sustain for a very, very long time.

Regardless of whether that vision sounds inspiring, or like the mythic perpetual motion machine, it has some very concrete applications. When we shift from the battery/recharge metaphor to the energy transaction narrative, we can shift from an emphasis on after-work recovery strategies and instead move our focus to the energy dynamics of our job.

Here's what we know—and really you have known this all along: willpower is a limited resource. All you have to do to demonstrate this fact is consider how long your New Year's resolutions lasted this time around. One month? One week? The self-control that willpower summons requires mental energy.

In a fascinating example of psychological principles being made manifest by neuro-physiological research, researchers found that glucose is depleted after an act requiring willpower (Gailliot et al., 2007). The amount of glucose within a cell is a limited commodity. Therefore, if you expend that glucose on an act that requires willpower, there is literally less energy available to exert willpower subsequently—at the cellular level. Let's be clear about this fact: you can't simply will yourself to do an excellent job for 30 years. In order to be sustainable, the work must provide as much energy—or more than—it demands.

Understanding energy as a two-way energy exchange provides us with some strategies. Specifically, it leads us to curiosity about where our energy goes—and where it comes from—during our days at work.

When was the last time your work required you to pick up anything heavier than 50 pounds? When was the last time you found yourself out of breath from exertion on your job? How much of your day do you spend outside of your climate-controlled office? I ask these questions—rhetorically of course—because when we say we do hard jobs, they aren't hard in the usual sense. When you stop to truly contemplate what makes trauma work difficult, it is because it is *emotionally demanding*. We do emotion work. We work with clients who are experiencing intense emotions. And secondary traumatic stress is produced by being within the "blast radius" of those feelings.

When carefully examined, however, the phenomenon of secondary trauma isn't really about the client's feelings at all. The feelings experienced by the client in response to their trauma are merely the reagent in this system. It is our emotional response to that reagent that produces strain, or stress, or secondary trauma. In other words, it is *our* emotions that produce secondary trauma. It is *our* efforts to manage our emotions that make this work difficult.

Emotional Labor and Emotion Strain

Emotional labor is a concept from the sociology and occupational psychology literature. It has great relevance to the emotion work that makes trauma therapy difficult. In the literature, emotional labor is defined as "the process by which workers are expected to manage their feelings in accordance with organizationally defined rules and guidelines" (Hochschild, 1983; Wharton, 2009). Emotional labor, then, is the effort that it takes to manage the difference between what you are required to express at work and what you actually feel. Emotional labor refers to the effort that we expend suppressing feelings, trying to change feelings, and trying to act one way (compassionate and professional) when we are actually feeling quite another (angry or overwhelmed). I will take a broad view of emotional labor in this chapter and conceptualize it as the energy that is expended to keep our emotions regulated: to maintain a professional demeanor when we feel sad, to recover after we have experienced a stressful experience, to get back into the "green zone" when we became dysregulated by a difficult experience. It takes effort to do these things—and we are doing it all day long.

A useful concept from the emotional labor literature is the concept of "emotion strain". Emotion strain refers to the effort required to display the desired emotion even though that emotion differs from your genuine emotion. In the emotion literature, this is referred to as "shallow acting": displaying an emotion that isn't genuine. And we shallow act all the time—and there is nothing wrong with that, our professional roles require it. And shallow acting can be the first step toward connecting with our genuine feelings.

Consider how much energy you expend straining to remain emotionally regulated, and acting professionally—when you are stressed, when you are experiencing strong feelings, when you are tired but trying to appear interested and caring, when you are frustrated by trying to appear patient, when you are angry but trying to appear compassionate. Emotion strain better describes the phenomenon that we have mischaracterized as "compassion fatigue". It is straining to get to compassion that is fatiguing, not the experience of genuine compassion. In fact—as we will see shortly—compassion is an energy *source*, not an energy drain.

Where Does Our Energy Go?

When we give up the distorted idea that work depletes, and leisure recharges, we can take a more accurate and nuanced view of our work energy. For starters, we know that activities with high emotional labor are depleting. What are the high emotional labor activities that we engage in during trauma therapy?

Emotion Strain from Working with Difficult, Angry, or Treatment-Resistant Clients

We choose our work because we are motivated to care for others. But sometimes our therapy efforts feel like an unintended game of tug-of-war. We maintain our customary calm demeanor and express empathy in all of the usual ways. But sometimes, that calm, accepting demeanor isn't congruent with our inner experience. Inside we may be frustrated with our client. We may be upset that she fails appointments and seems help-rejecting in many ways. Linehan (1993) refers to these behaviors as "therapy-interfering". We expect such reactions, because most of these behaviors are a result of the very trauma we are treating. We are able to formulate these behaviors through the trauma lens, and we understand them. But that doesn't mean we don't experience a considerable amount of emotion strain as we work toward a genuine calm and genuine empathy.

When I was in private practice, I was caring for a woman with a diagnosis of borderline personality disorder. She had been referred to me by her psychiatrist after being "fired" by three previous therapists. I met with her for three individual psychotherapy sessions, which had been filled with emotion strain for me. I found her to be very unrewarding, as she was combative and resistant, and gave very little back in the way of positive interaction or reason for hopefulness. To be honest, it was apparent to me why her previous therapists had terminated their treatment with her. But I was, nonetheless, committed to staying with her to get behind her defenses. She had predicted during our introductory session that I would quickly burn out with her too. I told her I would do everything I could to hang in with her.

Early in our fourth session, she said this to me: "I came to see you because Dr. Gardner told me you were good with women with my diagnosis. But I've watched you over the last three sessions, and I just have to say this: you're nothing special".

This is how I responded (it doesn't sound too bad, does it?): "Wow, it sounds like you are pretty disappointed in our work together so far. Thanks for letting me know; I think that is important information for me to have. Thanks for being honest about that because I definitely want to know if you are feeling that way".

So that is how I responded. I don't have a video, but I would hope that I sounded and appeared sincere. But it wasn't genuine. My genuine feeling was outrage—I felt betrayed that I had committed to do difficult work with her and that she had hurt me in return. For me to respond professionally was very emotionally straining. This is an example of emotional labor—this was highly laborious for me.

As I look at my response on paper years later, it looks okay. Although I didn't do any damage to my relationship with the client, it left me feeling drained and insincere. But I recovered during the subsequent week and approached her with a superior response. It was both genuine (which my first response was not) and helpful to my client. I will describe that response when we discuss strategies for reducing emotional labor.

Feeling Ineffective

As trauma therapists, we concern ourselves with complex clinical situations. Depending upon the setting in which you do your work, you may treat some of the most difficult clinical cases that we treat in psychotherapy. We are dealing with situations in which we are always hopeful, but we will not always succeed. Sometimes the clinical factors add up to an insoluble situation. Sometimes the change is slow to develop and may only be apparent years later. And usually, we are dealing with complex clients in the midst of their most symptomatic moments.

In order to maintain the desired narrative of advancing competence—and to keep up your motivation—you need a visible sign that you are accomplishing something. And sometimes, that visible evidence seems in short supply.

Dealing with difficult cases and rarely seeing dramatic changes can feel like we are swimming in the fog. And just like Florence Chadwick, we risk being beaten by not being able to see our progress. We stroke and stroke through our fatigue but don't know if we are getting any closer to our goal. This feeling of ineffectiveness is also high in emotional labor.

Being Overwhelmed by Complexity or Sheer Volume of Work

The sensation of being overwhelmed is a special focus in CE-CERT because it is one of the sources of secondary traumatic stress. When we "feel" overwhelmed, this doesn't help motivate us toward positive action. It is, rather, a freeze response—the most injurious of the stress responses. Therefore, when we are overwhelmed we are in the paradox of experiencing high emotional labor (the accelerator is pushed to the max) but we are not engaging in productive effort (the engine is disengaged).

Of particular focus are two circumstances that are extremely high in emotional labor: 1) when we are overwhelmed by the complexity or unfamiliarity of a task or client situation ("Wow, I don't even know where to start", or "I don't know what to do or say or what decision to make") and 2) when we are overwhelmed by the amount of work that we must do each day ("No matter how hard I work, I just can't get it all done").

Reducing Emotional Labor

If the three circumstances just described—emotion strain of working with difficult clients, feelings of ineffectiveness, and being overwhelmed—are major sources of high emotional labor, the task ahead of us is clear. Our job is to deconstruct these circumstances, so we can learn to allow each of them to become easier. Yes, it does require some effort upfront to change longtime patterns of thinking and acting. But ultimately, we are making our job easier.

It is a relatively simple intellectual task to deconstruct each of these high emotional labor situations. It is exhausting to strain to "act empathic" when you really are in conflict from working with difficult, angry, and resistant clients. It is draining to act like we feel in control and are feeling empathy when our genuine feelings are very far from that. And it isn't rewarding to work so hard for patients when we are frustrated or angry with them. Or even more so if—dare I speak the unspeakable?—we don't really like this client. And—if that is what high emotional labor looks like, what would low emotional labor look like?

The opposite of emotion strain is genuine emotion. Or, in the language of the emotional labor research, the opposite of shallow acting (acting like we feel something when we don't) is deep acting (using strategies to genuinely feel the expressed emotion). The emotional labor literature is replete with studies that demonstrate that while emotion strain is effortful, "deep acting" or genuine feelings reduce effort (Hülsheger et al., 2010; Mahoney et al., 2011). Genuine experience of emotions is *low* effort. More than low effort, experiencing genuine emotions is correlated with job engagement and enjoyment. Do I need to repeat how wrong we had it when we coined the term "compassion fatigue"?

Feeling ineffective is high in emotional labor. So, if we again conceptually reverse the feeling of ineffectiveness, where do we arrive? Effectiveness, of course—experiencing a sense that you are mastering the circumstance before you. Conceptually, it is really very simple: Doing something that you have mastered takes very little effort (emotional labor). But being in charge of a task that you don't know how to successfully complete is very difficult and therefore high in emotional labor. And even more so if the "task" is a life-and-death situation with a client.

With any task that you hate, it is worth considering what portion of that task aversion is attributable to a lack of mastery. You hate it because you hate the feeling of not knowing what to do.

Identify a task that you find aversive. Even better, write it down in this sentence: "I hate _____". Now flip it. Even though it may not be true—as an exercise—write it this way: "I am a master at _____".

Perhaps—because it will be true of many of us—you selected "documentation of services". Try it in the same form: "I hate completing the paperwork that this job requires". And try it on in the reverse: "I am a master at completing the paperwork that this job requires". It is hard to hate something that you have mastered. Even if it is something you will never truly enjoy, completing that task becomes less effortful because—if you have mastered it—you are now doing it in the most efficient manner. And, if nothing else, you are spending less time on it.

Using evidence-based practices reduces burnout and compassion fatigue. Even though learning and implementing a new way of practicing may appear highly effortful, studies consistently reveal that implementing these practices makes the work seem easier (Craig & Sprang, 2010; Kim et al., 2018; Wilkinson et al., 2017).

Burnout is mitigated by use of evidence-based approaches because focusing on a defined practice—one that has been demonstrated to be effective—increases our sense of efficacy. We know what to do, because the model defines that for us. When we aren't employing any particular model, we are much more likely to feel like we are playing whack-a-mole. The client throws out the issue-of-the-day, and we use our wits to try to contend with it. Sometimes we succeed, and sometimes we struggle. This is very effortful and makes it very difficult to create a narrative that we are making a steady advance toward a defined goal. And—if the promise of evidence-based approaches is valid—we may feel more effective because we simply *are* more effective.

And last, what is the result of reverse engineering the sense of being overwhelmed by how complex our cases are, or the sheer amount of work we are expected to complete? Let's start with the first source of that sensation—being overwhelmed by complexity. As you work in the trauma field, you undoubtedly work with complex cases. It is a given of the work. If that sometimes feels overwhelming, examine where the overwhelm is coming from. Can you entertain—even for a moment—the possibility that the complexity of these cases can be endlessly challenging and infinitely fascinating? In other words, why is the complexity of the cases daunting rather than stimulating?

Trauma treatment is a field so complex that however long you have been doing it, you will continue to learn and get better each year. This can be overwhelming—you will never completely master this job or feel like you have learned enough. But it also can be viewed as a perk of the job. Surgeons reach peak effectiveness from 1 to 15 years into their work (depending on the surgical procedure). Plumbers and electricians are considered "masters" of their trade between 6 and 9 years on the job. At what point does a trauma therapist reach peak effectiveness? I would argue that there is no upper limit. And further, I would suggest that it is most helpful for you to cultivate and maintain the feeling that you will be better next year at your craft than you are this year.

But subscribing to—and benefitting from—that belief requires that you develop an acceptance of not always knowing all there is about trauma work, or this client, or this situation. Everything becomes easier when we can settle into the knowledge that we—at the same time—know enough, and don't know it all.

One of the passionately committed psychotherapists that I interviewed told an intriguing story. She described a time when her supervisor assigned her to take over a DBT (Dialectical Behavior Therapy) group to replace the group leader who had unexpectedly resigned. She protested strongly, citing her lack of knowledge about DBT. "I always have to throw a hissy fit first", she told me, "then I relax and solve the problem". She went into the first group with DBT manuals for all of the group members. "We are going to learn this together", she told them, "because I don't know much about this model. But I know how to do therapy, so we are going to do well". She concluded her description of this event by saying it was one of her favorite clinical experiences.

Employing a model about which you are unknowledgeable isn't a best practice in implementing DBT or any other evidence-based practice. But this therapist's confidence is a model for contending with certain types of overwhelm. "I don't know enough—but I know how to do therapy". And sometimes it's okay to declare that you are stuck, that you don't know what to do or say. And always it is okay to request consultation from a supervisor or team. Suddenly it can be easier when I realize you don't have to resolve this in this instant. I can defer to the next session. I can even ask the client to wait until I seek consultation. And when I realize the immediate pressure is off, I can begin to enjoy the fact that I will continue to develop in this expert role.

Being overwhelmed by workload requires a very particular type of equanimity to resolve. It begins with a truism: you work in a role that will never be completely finished. Most days, you don't go home because you did everything. You leave because it is time; you leave because you saw your last scheduled client. But not because you accomplished everything that you could possibly accomplish.

You won't naturally have the feeling that you are done. Rather, you will—and you have—set personal limits. Equanimity refers to the ability to remain calm in the midst of difficulty. I would transduce that definition into the language of emotional labor by saying that equanimity is the ability to find ease in situations that others might find effortful. One of the greatest challenges for most of us in many work settings is resolving the difference between our personal limits and organizational expectations.

The first step is to identify the difference: is this sense of being overwhelmed by your workload because you are trying to do too much? Or is that stress coming from the supervisory/organizational requirement for a workload that is higher than you are emotionally or physically equipped to tolerate?

It is critical that you make explicit your personal limits. Is your perfectionism or unrealistic need to save the world the reason you are operating beyond your personal limits? *All just organizations will accept workloads that are reasonable to accomplish.* It may be up to you to declare the zone between your comfort and your mission orientation. Not less, and not more. If this is not an acceptable workload to your organization, then your decision to remain equates to a decision to accept this level of overwhelm. We will soon discuss that important question about making the decision about your work with wholeheartedness.

We can imagine the emotional labor of our work operating within a force field. It comes down to the mechanics of a simple machine: how heavy is the weight, and how much force do we apply? Adding weight to our role are factors like uncertainty about how to do our jobs (and our level of acceptance of uncertainty); how pleasant or unpleasant we find our work to be, or feelings of disengagement from our sense of mission. Within this mechanical system, the upward lift is provided by our sense of efficacy and mastery, experiencing the work with a positive valence, or a felt sense of personal meaning in the work.

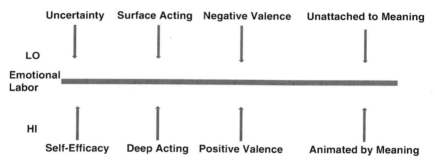

By no means does this description exhaust all of the restraining and energizing factors related to our emotional labor. But it illustrates the fact that the amount of labor that our work requires is not a fixed volume. Some of our job tasks are not only relatively light, but they actually lift *us* up. And others may be extremely heavy for reasons we should carefully analyze. Are we adding weight in ways we haven't acknowledged? Some of our work is simply heavy, and it always will be. But overall, are there ways to both lighten the weight of this work and to increase the amount of force we are applying.

Reducing emotional labor won't result in boundless energy. I'm not promising that you will, every day, come home thrumming with excess energy. Your physical and emotional energy is very complex and multifactorial. Your energy will be affected by how much sleep you had, how much stress you have in your life, and how much exertion you gave all day. But it is fruitful to pay attention to your sense of being tired, being depleted. If it is a natural response to a day filled with exertion—what we sometimes describe as "leaving it all on the field", that is a desirable state.

You will recognize this state because—although you are tired, your emotional state will tilt toward a calm, even pleasant mood. Contrast that with a sense of being fatigued from emotional labor. This state will create a sense of detachment and lethargy, and your emotional state will tilt toward sadness, numbness or even depression. This is a sign that you have spent your day suppressing feelings associated with emotional labor.

Turning Concepts to Skills

Turning these principles into the project of reducing emotional labor begins—again—with setting an intention. I like seeing our intention within this skill domain as "learning to participate in joyful work". That is quite a different goal than a father's ethic of "It's not supposed to be fun; that is why we call it work". Your job—because you are a trauma therapist—contains the right components to allow your work to be joyful. That is because it *is* difficult work. The most rewarding work will always be that which requires our full attention and engagement. Rewards will never be derived from a demand-less state.

Your job is profound. And it offers the pleasures of human interaction and the possibility of witnessing the triumph of brave people. So, all the right elements are there. What we need, then, to experience our work as joyful is to reduce the strain that depletes our energy and our enjoyment of this work. I want to accentuate this intention by saying that this is my favorite of our targets that we will establish in any of the chapters: to have *joyful work*. We have the term "labor of love" in the common vernacular to describe work that is low in emotional labor. I hope that you will take a moment to find some pleasure even in envisioning this as your goal. We aren't going to have to work harder. We are going to begin to work easier.

Radical Compassion

Emotion strain accounts for a significant portion of our total emotional labor. Recall that emotion strain is produced by the dissonance between the emotion that you are displaying and the genuine emotions (and thoughts) that you are experiencing. The opposite of emotion strain is authentic emotion: feeling what you are expressing and expressing what you are feeling. Once you allow yourself to do both of these things—and once you learn *how* to do both of these—working with difficult clients gets considerably easier. Emotional labor is reduced. Scores of studies of emotional labor demonstrate this point. So, the question really is how do I: 1) have genuine emotion for clients I am naturally frustrated with, angry at, or find aversive; and 2) express my genuine thoughts and feelings without damage to the therapeutic relationship?

Radical compassion begins with an intention-within-this-intention. What makes this form of compassion radical is that you are establishing a goal of offering compassion *to every client that you work with*. Even before you have met the client you will begin therapy with next Thursday, you already have a goal to experience—or to cultivate—compassion for them. You don't know what their demeanor will be. You don't know what their degree of motivation for change is, or their level of engagement. You don't know what their history is, or what they look like.

In 1964, Professor William Schofield suggested that mental health professionals are biased toward the so-called "YAVIS" patient: Young, attractive, verbal, intelligent, and successful (Schofield, 1964). A person with that profile is likely going to be favored in all things. And we can understand why therapists would want verbal, highly motivated clients who can energetically engage in treatment. But many of your clients won't fit that description. The YAVIS client may be the most like you—but they are not the ones who need you the most.

Now consider the inverse of the YAVIS client. A client who is aging, not physically attractive, inarticulate, below average in intelligence, and unemployed. When you see that profile on paper, you may see how it might be hard to naturally experience compassion for this tough client—maybe the profile makes you more tired than compassionate. Or maybe this profile actually elicits more compassion from you, because you can see that this person has been dealt a tough hand for success in this world. But let's add a few characteristics to the profile: this man is also quite hostile and entitled. He doesn't express gratitude for anything that you do for him, and in fact, is frequently critical.

What is your inner experience as you summon an image of this man? Is it compassion? In concept, I have described traits that contribute to life difficulties for this person, and therefore make him more in need of our compassion. But in practice, it is hard to feel compassion if you are feeling resentful of his sense of entitlement, and defensive in response to his criticisms. And that is what makes a client like this high in emotional labor.

Let's return to your *intention*: are you willing to allow or, if necessary, to cultivate compassion for him? The promise is that genuine compassion will ease your emotion strain. Assuming that you don't *feel* compassion naturally for this man, are you *willing* to experience compassion? Is your narrative that he will be entitled to your compassion if, and only if, he shows a little gratitude for all that you are trying to do for him? In other words, what is the *quid pro quo* that you require in order to offer your compassion? Do you require pleasantness? Do you require gratitude? Do you require that the client not present problems that seem insurmountable? That they smell good? That they describe something sad enough that you can empathize?

Each of these requirements—indeed imposing any requirement in order to get compassionate care—might be conceptualized as a compassion tax: I will give you my compassion when you have paid the compassion tax. And for those who don't pay the tax but instead display defensive, resistant, disorganized or other difficult behavior, I will withhold my compassion. And that means I will experience emotion strain. My work will remain effortful with these clients. And—depending on the clientele I work with, and the tax that I require—I may have a lot of high-effort clients in my work.

Radical compassion eliminates the compassion tax. Radical compassion is the principle that my work will only be effective when I can contact genuine compassion for my client. And if caring is genuine, I won't have to expend effort on shallow acting, so it seems like I care. The first step in turning this concept into a skill is for you to decide if you can accept compassion that is this radical. Can you agree that all of your clients are entitled to your compassion? Some will elicit it naturally, and for others you will have to demonstrate emotional skillfulness to cultivate genuine caring.

Jaak Panskepp founded the field of affective neuroscience, the study of the biological basis of emotions. His work identified the basic emotional systems in the brain—the circuitry and the neuro-facilitating chemicals. One of those emotional circuits is the "caring" circuit. This circuit essentially identifies the mechanism, the location, and the actual material of which compassion is made. The circuits involved in the brain that are active during the experience of caring for another is the anterior cingulate, BNST, preoptic hypothalamus, VMH, and PAC. The neuromodulators of this feeling are oxytocin, prolactin, dopamine, and the opioids. You don't have to understand brain anatomy and neurotransmission to understand why these circuits and these neurotransmitters are significant: 1) our brain has evolved specific circuitry dedicated to the emotions of "caring" or compassion; and 2) compassion is a deeply pleasurable experience—at the cellular level. Once again, compassion fatigue was the entirely wrong concept. If we experience compassion for a client, it isn't effortful to care for them. Indeed, it *adds energy*—and pleasure—to our work.

Compassion, as I conceptualize it here, is not only a virtue. Rather, it is a skill that can be cultivated. This removes the notion that compassion is just a squishy, nice idea. Compassion has been empirically demonstrated to be an essential and necessary element in effective treatment, albeit in the language of related concepts such as "therapeutic alliance" or "empathy". Once we make radical compassion our target—and view compassion as a skill, not just being a virtuous person—our ability to experience compassion can be enhanced. And when we increase our level of compassion, there is a resulting decrease in the amount of emotional labor we are exerting in the caring relationship. Compassion-as-skill can be conceptualized as a series of seven switches that enable us to turn the compassion on, or to turn it off:

Compassion Switch #1: On Switch: Intention of Radical Compassion—Off Switch: "Earned Compassion"

The first of the compassion "switches" is the intention toward radical compassion. Honestly and directly establishing this goal turns on our capacity for compassion. So, take a moment right now and consider your willingness to establish this intention—are you willing to extend compassion for each and every one of your clients simply as a part of your role, not something the client must earn? The first "off switch" is judgement, the aforementioned compassion tax. "He's not even trying". "She is just Axis II". Our compassion switch is in the off position unless our client does something to turn our compassion on in this condition.

Compassion Switch #2: On Switch: Stepping Out of the "Drama Triangle"—Off Switch: Looking for "Perpetrators"

The second switch enabling radical compassion is the insight and willingness to step out of the "drama" triangle. In 1968, psychiatrist Stephen Karpman described the drama triangle that authors used to develop drama in fairytales. He noted how, in dramatic human relationships, our roles are defined in the same triangle of 1) victim, 2) perpetrator, and 3) rescuer (although those roles sometimes switch). In order to turn the compassion switch on, we can't assign our client the role of perpetrator (Karpman, 1968).

Our brain tends to define the world in terms of who the victim is and who the perpetrator is, and we—as therapists—often are motivated to play the role of rescuer. That may be helpful in some contexts. But we can't be helpful to our client if we have cast them in the role of perpetrator. That makes us—or someone else, such as the client's child or partner—the victim. Identifying these roles strikes the stage for the drama triangle. We cannot help our client from this schema because we will not be able to access compassion. Our impulse will be to withdraw or to punish.

Working in children's behavioral health, the clients for whom I had the most difficulty experiencing compassion were the parents whom I believed were too cold or too punitive toward their child. When I had the parent cast in the role of the perpetrator, I would feel compassion for the child (victim) but be unable to be helpful to the parent (perpetrator). If I am honest—if we as therapists collectively are honest—some of our motivation to this work is that we crave the role of rescuer. Sometimes that serves us by motivating us to action. But this role is counterproductive when our client is viewed as the perpetrator. I wanted to rescue the child—but I couldn't—because I had no compassion for the parent. By giving up the ability to connect with the parent, I had sacrificed my ability to change the circumstances for the child.

When we explicitly identify the drama triangle in which we are operating, our goal becomes clear: to find compassion for the one we identified as perpetrator, not only the one we cast as victim. Our goal is transformed when we see the way in which the perpetrator is also a victim. Once I became conscious of my tendency to see the world in terms of the drama triangle, I found it was typically quite easy to see the way in which the parent—whom I had cast as the "bad guy"—was trapped by circumstance. Often, these individuals have their own trauma history. Our compassion will be firmly in the "off" position if we remain committed to this view of perpetrator and victim in the relationships.

Compassion Switch #3: On Switch: Noticing and Acknowledging Genuine Feelings—Off Switch: Suppressing or Denying Genuine Feelings

The third switch that activates our capacity for radical compassion is another "radical" idea—the practice of scrupulously noticing and acknowledging our *genuine* feelings. This is radical behavior because we aim to acknowledge and accept our feelings whatever they may be—positive or negative, caring or hostile. In the emotional labor literature, a distinction is made between shallow acting (which is effortful) and deep acting, which is a genuine experience of the emotion and that is, therefore, low effort. (I would add a third: spontaneous, genuine emotion.) For some of your clients, you will experience compassionate caring without any effort. Because of a match of their personal characteristics and yours, caring will naturally arise. For others, your initial, genuine emotion will be something else—frustration, impatience, judgment.

There is nothing wrong with you that you sometimes have judgmental, critical feelings. I have a colleague who says to his supervisees, "You don't have to fix your feelings. They aren't broken". Or, as the Buddha said, "Don't push the river". The central concept in emotional labor is that suppressing and denying those feelings takes tremendous effort.

As a clinical supervisor, I always felt a sense of relief when one of my supervisees would confide—often reluctantly, "To be honest, I don't really like her". I wasn't critical of that feeling—I was *relieved* to hear it expressed. I felt relieved because now that sentiment is out there, in the space before us—acknowledged and not the least bit dangerous. Implicitly understood between us was that the therapist wouldn't remain passive about disliking her client, but for now, it is where she was. Now that the feeling was acknowledged, it would not be acted out—the client will be kept safe. Not only did I, as a supervisor, experience relief to hear this genuineness, but the therapist would also experience a sense of relief as the energy used to suppress the "unspeakable" was released. In order for our compassion switch to be on, we have to be in touch with and willing to acknowledge our genuine feelings. If we suppress or deny those feelings, we cannot get to genuine caring—we will use all of our energy shallow acting.

Compassion Switch #4: On Switch: Curiosity and Model of Mind—Off Switch: Reactivity

If you work with clients with a trauma history, then you work with a certain percentage of clients who are sometimes defensive, resistant, and help-rejecting. We trauma therapists accept that these styles result from the trauma itself. Therefore, it shouldn't be surprising or outrageous when the client is any of those things. Understanding the worldview that explains these behavioral styles is very much what trauma therapists do. But emotional labor is high if, when we are working with these difficult behaviors, we are pushing against them. Or if we are judgmental about our client's style or worldview. Or if we feel personally defensive.

I will return to the client I described earlier as she told me, "I've watched you over the last three sessions, and I just have to say: you're nothing special". I've already acknowledged that my genuine emotion was anger. I attribute that now to my lack of seasoning as a trauma therapist. Because when I summon that memory now, it makes me smile. She actually was right—I'm not anything special (don't tell my mom; she maintained that I am very special). So why, then, did it make me defensive when my client said I wasn't special? My defensiveness about that is the source of how effortful it was to maintain a professional, non-reactive demeanor.

As soon as I dis-identify from my sense of specialness, it becomes possible to feel compassion for my client. Curiosity about the client's worldview turns the radical compassion switch to the on position. Defensiveness and reactivity turn that switch off. It is easy for me, from this distance in time, to become curious about that patient's comment. It is easy for me now to build a model of mind of this woman. Having already been "fired" by three therapists, she was testing me—how would I respond to this jab? Would this provoke a crisis in which I fired her—which she believed was just getting the inevitable over with? Or would I remain therapeutically engaged with her—which would help establish a sense of security? As soon as I become involved in building this model of mind, my defensiveness goes away, and my curiosity grows.

Such curiosity—the act of constructing the "model of mind" of the client is the fourth compassion switch. Building a model of mind of difficult behavior—"Oh, that is why she does that..."— isn't yet genuine empathy, but it lays the framework for genuineness. Possessing an intellectual understanding of the function of my client's difficult behavior allows for cognitive empathy. And—just as important, the act of curiosity and problem solving are functions of the pre-frontal cortex. I become less reactive when I am in problem-solving mode. I get calmer—and that creates the conditions that can allow for empathy to develop—from cognitive empathy to genuine, experienced caring. As long as I am being reactive and defensive, however, this switch remains in the "off" position.

Compassion Switch #5: On Switch: Connectedness—Off Switch: Separateness

Sometimes we psychologically separate ourselves from our clients because we believe we need to defend ourselves from them. Sometimes we become judgmental about behaviors to which we cannot relate. Our ability to experience compassion is turned off when we do that. On the other hand, the compassion switch is on when we feel connected to the client. A Buddhist practice to help us connect to others is, during meditation, to chant "Just like me..." As in, "Just like me, she wants to be happy". "Just like me, she wants to feel safe". "Oh, she is angry because she feels misunderstood. I do that too..." "Oh, she is impatient. I recognize that feeling..."

Because of course she does want to be safe and happy—all of us do. Perhaps she is not successful in creating this feeling for herself, but we certainly can understand the desire to be happy. And we can identify with feelings of being frustrated, being misunderstood, being impatient, and being poorly treated by others. She is, indeed, just like me—and if I make her "other", I will not be able to experience genuine compassion.

Compassion Switch #6: On Switch: Behavioral Strategies—Off Switch—Fight or Flight

Another compassion switch is available to us when we are struggling to experience genuine compassion: employing a behavioral strategy that helps us move to the emotional "green zone". Fight or flight in response to difficult behaviors turns the compassion switch off. That makes sense—we don't want to experience compassion for someone who represents a threat to us. If we are physically threatened, we should not be seeking compassion. Our only consideration is establishing physical safety. But when these threats are to our identity, or to our patience, our first goal is to resolve the fight or flight stress response. Compassion lives in the prefrontal cortex—it can only be accessed when we feel emotionally safe.

Behavioral strategies can be very simple, or very intentional formal practices. When you realize that you are reactive, step back to take a pause and drop back into yourself. Notice what is happening inside your body. Notice your breathing—follow a few breaths. Let yourself come back into your body again.

I have had success employing a Tonglen method when I found myself becoming frustrated or angry with a client. I won't go deeply into Tonglen here, except to offer this simple technique: while following your breath, chant inwardly during the inhale, "I am breathing in the anger" and, on the exhale, "I am breathing out compassion and acceptance". This was a truly centering exercise for me. It works because it brings me back into my body; it establishes my intention toward compassion. It creates an image of transforming negative feelings into compassion, and the deep, purposeful breathing brings me back into my green zone.

Compassion Switch #7: On Switch: Rehearsed Compassion—Off Switch: Reactivity

The last compassion switch is indicated for those clients for whom you have significant difficulty finding compassion. If you find that you are continually reactive with a certain client, it will be difficult to find compassion. That is, of course, the formula for high emotional labor. It is physiologically impossible to be reactive and compassionate at the same time. That is why if you are constantly feeling provoked during your interaction with this client, you may need to find compassion *before* you interact with him. Practicing compassion in a methodical and intentional way before your interaction with the client will allow you to bring the compassion with you into the session. Practice though imagery during a meditation or when you are calm and relaxed. Use any of the "compassion switches" I have described: Tonglen: "breathe in defensiveness, breathe out compassion"; or practice connection: "just like me, he wants to be happy"; or build a model of mind of the difficult behavior. Your goal is to experience a moment of compassion when you aren't under duress. Then—as in the sport psychology technique—after imagining the perfect performance, carry this felt memory into your engagement with the client.

I conclude this section on radical compassion by returning to my experience with my client who told me "you're nothing special". I'm satisfied with how I responded in that moment, but it was very emotionally effortful. After taking the intervening week to prepare for my next session with her, I had a superior—and radically genuine—response. I began our session with this authentic expression: "You remember how, when we began our work together, you predicted I would burn out on you, and I told you I would try my best to stay here for you? After our last session, I noticed I was feeling depleted when you told me I hadn't been helpful. So, I realized that I need to make a request of you: if I succeed in doing anything helpful for you, would you let me know? That would put a lot in my tank and help me know I was on the right course. I think I could run for a long time on that".

It was a genuine (low emotional labor) expression. And it transformed the nature of our therapeutic relationship. She couldn't have responded better—and I felt a huge surge of energy as I ceased repressing my resentment. For the first time, I became capable of compassion for her.

Wholeheartedness

Brother David Steindl-Rast made a profound and unexpected point that contributes an important idea to our analysis of energy gain/loss during our work. Speaking on burnout he said, "The cure for exhaustion is not necessarily rest. It is wholeheartedness" (Rabke, 2017). This wisdom contradicts popular concepts of burnout. It is, however, utterly consistent with the empirical evidence on burnout—and emotional labor. Engagement is the diametric opposite of burnout—full engagement is another way of describing wholeheartedness.

This chapter is about finding joyful work. Challenge yourself honestly: are you ambivalent about your work? Do you retreat from stressful moments into the fantasy of just walking away and finding another line of work? The TV character Ron Swanson gave advice less elegantly than Steindl-Rast, but just as apt: "Never half-ass two things. Whole-ass one thing" (Daniels, Schur & Hiscock, 2012).

When was the last time you wondered if you were in the right job? Determining whether you are in the right job is an entirely fair and profound question. But if you are putting energy into asking yourself that question every time you have a stressful experience, or a bad day, that is without doubt where much of your energy is being lost. If you approach your work each day with ambivalence, you are driving with one foot on the gas and one on the brake. Of course, work will be depleting as long as some of your energy goes one direction and some of your energy creates an opposing drag. It is a matter of simple physics.

The beginning of a solution comes from the stoic philosopher Seneca, "Ponder for a long time whether you shall admit a given person to your friendship; but when you have decided to admit him, welcome him with all your heart and soul". I will repurpose that statement: "Ponder deeply and sincerely if you have found your vocation. If your answer is yes, engage the work with all your heart and soul". And—perhaps this goes without saying—if your answer is no, apply the same wholeheartedness to making a career change. This sounds more cut-and-dried than I want it to. But the fact is that you simply cannot flourish in this work—cannot find joy in it—if you approach it half-heartedly. Your energy cannot maintain such division of effort over time.

You don't have to make a commitment for an entire career. Of course, you can—and should— reconsider as circumstances change. Decide how often you will conduct this reflection—annually? Until there are major changes in your life or in your work environment? But you cannot afford to remain ambivalent over the entirety of your career.

In order to find your way to wholehearted commitment, you must remind yourself that you have *chosen* to do this work. The only alternative is resentment and the resulting feeling that you are a hostage to your work. From an energy dynamic perspective, a tremendous amount of energy is lost when there is a 50% drag on the system—the part of you that doesn't want to do this—over the work day.

I have attempted to place the CE-CERT domains into the context of concepts-into-skills. But wholeheartedness is an exception. Wholeheartedness isn't really a skill. It is the mental practice of catching yourself "amibivalating" about your commitment to your job. Then, it becomes conceptually quite simple. Steindl-Rast says, "All you need to do is do the same thing that you are doing now, but wholeheartedly". When you commit wholeheartedly, all of your energy moves in one direction. The weight becomes easier to lift because you are using both hands.

Radical Acceptance and Intentional Learning

The final skill for reducing emotional labor begins with careful consideration of the job roles and tasks that are—for you—high in emotional labor. Once you have identified these tasks—and you have analyzed what, exactly, makes them high in emotional demand, you can re-engineer them to reduce the load they are placing on you. This re-engineering consists of: 1) radical acceptance (yes, another radical concept); and 2) intentional learning.

Raymond Dlugos conducted a qualitative study with passionately committed psychologists (Dlugos & Friedlander, 2001). He described one passionate psychologist who was asked what he most disliked about his job. He explained—as will many psychotherapists—that he used to hate the documentation requirements that insurance companies imposed upon him. Like many of us, he described how he would say to himself that this wasn't why he went into this work—to do paperwork. But one day, he said, "I decided to stop resisting and to 'render unto Caesar that which is Caesar's.'" He decided to give up the resistance, and to become as efficient at completing paperwork as possible. His goal was to lessen the time drain so he could focus better on serving the mission about which he was passionate: his patients. "And you know what?" he said, "Now I kind of enjoy it". He had successfully transformed a task that had been high in emotional labor into one that is low in emotional labor.

This psychologist's strategy illustrates two ways we can reduce the labor we are investing in aversive tasks: 1) radically accepting that these tasks are part of work whether we like them or not (and whether we agree that they *should* be part of our jobs or not); and 2) intentional learning—reframing the aversive task into a skills challenge.

My own study of passionately committed psychotherapists revealed that they often performed the same two actions when they encounter aversive tasks. I would ask what part of their job they found energy-depleting, and they often would volunteer a similar story of giving up the resistance and then developing skills to make the job less aversive.

One of the therapists I interviewed described that his big energy drain had been dealing with angry, disgruntled consumers—often family members of clients. "I decided I needed to learn everything I could about how to deal with angry clients". After reading a great deal of literature on the topic and even attending a conference on the subject, he instructed the receptionist, "If there is a disgruntled person here, have them talk to me. You can even interrupt me if necessary, and I will come out". He discovered that he was very good at defusing angry people. "It really just comes down to one thing: find something that you can validate in what they are saying", he told me. And, he said further, "I think this is one of my favorite parts of my job now—it is so rewarding to see these angry people transformed once they feel validated". He also successfully transformed a high emotional labor task into one that is low in emotional labor—it became easy for him.

Here is a journal title you don't expect to see: "Enriched Environment Exposure Accelerates Rodent Driving Skills". And maybe you aren't terribly interested in learning more about rodent driving skills. But this fascinating study revealed the chemical underpinnings of the importance of intentional learning and how it eases emotional labor. More specifically, the research revealed the biological underpinnings of stress reduction as we acquire new skills. In this study, researchers taught rats to drive small cars by touching a copper wire to cause it to stop, start, and steer. Apparently, the rats did learn how to make the car go and even navigate—but rodent driving really isn't my emphasis here. Rather, my interest is in describing the researcher's findings that rats who had learned how to drive their "rat mobile" had increased their emotional resilience. This was demonstrated by the fact that they had lower amounts of the stress hormone corticosterone, and higher amounts of dehydroepiandrosterone, an anti-stress hormone, compared to the controls (Crawford et al., 2020).

Passionately committed therapists often practice radical acceptance and intentional learning naturally—they notice the parts of their jobs that they are struggling with (high emotional labor); then, they go through a process of accepting that, aversive or not, this task is simply part of this job. Then, they set about learning how to do that thing better (intentional learning.) This two-fold strategy confers multiple benefits toward our goal of making our jobs feel less effortful: 1) Through acceptance, we conserve effort that we would have expended resisting, "This isn't what I signed up for!" 2) As we master the task, it often feels less aversive. In some cases, it even becomes pleasant. 3) As illustrated by the "rat mobile" study, development of mastery enhances our resilience and increases our sense of task satisfaction. It feels good to feel like we are always learning and always advancing in our skillfulness. And it certainly feels good to notice that we are spending less times on jobs we hate.

Becoming more skillful at the strategies for reducing emotional labor may itself be effortful—I realize I am suggesting *more* emotional labor initially. Changing long-time patterns does expend energy. But each of these skills is in the service of ultimately making your job more pleasant and less effortful. Success here holds the promise of equalizing the energy *demands* of your work with the job *satisfactions* that your work provides—that is worth an upfront investment of some of your precious energy.

Reconsider the emotional labor-reducing skills that I have introduced: 1) becoming compassionate for all of your clients, 2) approaching your work with undivided commitment, and 3) accepting the reality that your work includes some aversive elements, and learning to relish the opportunity for life-long learning. When you reconsider that list, you will see that ultimately what makes the job easier is developing our own heart for the work. And what more pleasant task can you imagine than energetically transforming work as profound as ours into joyful work?

Reducing Emotional Labor

You Must Remember This

- Emotional labor is defined as the effort that it takes to demonstrate a desired, socially accepted emotion.

    - When we express an emotion that is different than our genuine emotion, it produces emotion strain. Emotion strain is very effortful. Genuine emotional expression, on the other hand, actually adds energy.

- The narrative that our energy battery is charged at home and depleted at work is unhelpful and inaccurate. This narrative needs to be replaced by one of energy exchange between tasks that confer energy and tasks that consume energy. Work is not comprised solely of energy discharge; it also contains many sources of energy. Ultimately, in order to flourish in our work, we must be able to derive energy from the work.

- High emotional labor situations include:

    - Emotion strain from working with difficult clients: trying to remain emotionally regulated while working with clients who may be resistant, difficult to treat, therapy-interfering, or angry and help-rejecting
    - Feeling ineffective
    - Being overwhelmed

        - By the complexity of client situations
        - By sheer volume of workload

Bridging Concepts to Skills

Emotional labor can be reduced by increasing three capacities:

- Radical Compassion: High effort is required when we "shallow act" by trying to appear accepting and caring when really, we are frustrated, angry, or judgmental. Genuine compassion reduces this effort:

    - Establish a goal of "radical compassion"
    - Step out of the "drama triangle"
    - Acknowledge genuine feelings
    - Develop curiosity and a model of mind
    - Find connection
    - Try behavioral approaches
    - Use rehearsed compassion

- Wholeheartedness

    - Wholeheartedness is moving beyond any ambivalence we may have about our work so we can fully and energetically engage the tasks we are doing. It is not about doing anything you aren't already doing—it is just committing to do it with your full heart and mind.

- Radical Acceptance and Intentional Learning
Radical acceptance and intentional learning are the two steps that help reduce the amount of emotional labor required by the aversive aspects of your work.

  - Radical acceptance is letting go of the resistance and narratives that oppose the challenging elements of our work (documentation and bureaucratic demands, difficult clients, etc.). Acceptance occurs when we change those narratives: "I don't like it, but it's just part of my job".
  - Intentional learning is re-directing the thoughts and energy resisting the unpleasant task into learning how to become more skillful in accomplishing the task. In the best case, we may actually convert some aversive tasks into pleasant tasks as we become more skillful. In the least case, we become more efficient at getting the tasks out of our way without losing a great deal of energy that would have gone into resisting.

Reducing Emotional Labor

Self-Audit

1. Think of a client for whom you had difficulty experiencing compassion. Consider why you didn't naturally feel empathy for him/her. Here are some possibilities:

   a. Their level of anxiety or "neediness" made you feel anxious.
   b. They had problems that overwhelmed you because you didn't know what to do.
   c. They seemed unmotivated or "help-rejecting".
   d. They had mannerisms that reminded you of someone that you don't like.
   e. You felt threatened by them.
   f. You felt judgmental about choices they were making or the way they acted.

2. Still considering the client you identified above:

   a. Are you willing to offer them "radical compassion"?
   b. What is this person fighting for? In what way do you imagine that they feel trapped by circumstances or by their worldview?
   c. What barrier do you have to overcome in yourself to move toward radical compassion for them?

3. When was the last time you asked yourself if you wanted to continue doing your job? Was it a serious decision, or was it more in fantasy?

How much energy are you expending to this question that keeps "one foot in and one foot out" of the work?

4. Identify an aspect of your job that you resent. _____

   a. Now imagine letting the resentment go and radically accepting that this task will not change.

      i.   Now you will let it be merely part of the "housekeeping" part of the job. Can you save time by not having the internal narrative about why you dislike doing it before you dive into this task? Does this free any energy?

      ii. Are there elements of this task at which you could get better or more efficient?

5. What are the "energy dementors" that drain your energy? What activities give you more energy than they require from you? Can the energy dementors be transformed with conscious attention, or are they the "shovel work" that must be radically accepted?

6. Consider the last day you came home from work feeling emotionally drained. What was the quality of that fatigue? Did you feel like you had an unproductive day? Were you numb and sluggish? Or did you feel like you had been productive, but had given all you had to the work that day? (The first kind of fatigue—feeling numb or logy—is a sign of high emotional labor. The second kind of fatigue is the desirable kind—being tired because we worked hard.)

Descriptive Statements:

Gray	I never feel more myself than when I am doing my job.
	It is almost always a pleasure to do this work.
Light Gray	I occasionally question if I would have been happier doing something else.
	I sometimes have to work hard to put on my "happy face" when I'm at work.
Black	I don't know how much longer I can continue to do this.

References

Ben-Shahar, T. (2007). *Happier: Learn the secrets to daily joy and lasting fulfillment*. New York: McGraw-Hill Companies.

Clark, P. (2009). Resiliency in the practicing marriage and family therapist. *Journal of Marital and Family Therapy, 35*(2), 231–247.

Craig, C. D., & Sprang, G. (2010). Compassion satisfaction, compassion fatigue, and burnout in a national sample of trauma treatment therapists. *Anxiety, Stress, & Coping, 23*(3), 319–339.

Crawford, L. E., Knouse, L. E., Kent, M., Vavra, D., Harding, O., LeServe, D., & Lambert, K. G. (2020). Enriched environment exposure accelerates rodent driving skills. *Behavioural Brain Research, 378*, 112309.

Daniels, G., Schur, M., Hiscock, N. (Writers), & Schur, M. (Director). (2012, February 23). Sweet Sixteen. [Televison episode]. In Daniels, G., Schur, M., Klein, H., Sackett, M., Holland, D., & Goor, D. (Producers), *Parks and Recreation*. Los Angeles, NBC.

Dlugos, R. F., & Friedlander, M. L. (2001). Passionately committed psychotherapists: A qualitative study of their experiences. *Professional Psychology: Research and Practice, 32*(3), 298.

Gailliot, M. T., Baumeister, R. F., DeWall, C. N., Maner, J. K., Plant, E. A., Tice, D. M., & Schmeichel, B. J. (2007). Self-control relies on glucose as a limited energy source: Willpower is more than a metaphor. *Journal of Personality and Social Psychology, 92*(2), 325.

Hochschild, A. R. (1983). *The managed heart: Commercialization of human feeling*. Berkeley: University of California Press.

Hülsheger, U. R., Lang, J. W., & Maier, G. W. (2010). Emotional labor, strain, and performance: Testing reciprocal relationships in a longitudinal panel study. *Journal of Occupational Health Psychology, 15*(4), 505.

Karpman, S. (1968). Fairy tales and script drama analysis. *Transactional Analysis Bulletin, 7*(26), 39–43.

Kim, J. J., Brookman-Frazee, L., Gellatly, R., Stadnick, N., Barnett, M. L., & Lau, A. S. (2018). Predictors of burnout among community therapists in the sustainment phase of a system-driven implementation of multiple evidence-based practices in children's mental health. *Professional Psychology: Research and Practice, 49*(2), 132.

Linehan, M. M. (1993). *Dialectical behavioral therapy of borderline personality disorder*. New York: Guilford.

Mahoney, K. T., Buboltz Jr, W. C., Buckner V. J. E., & Doverspike, D. (2011). Emotional labor in American professors. *Journal of Occupational Health Psychology, 16*(4), 406.

Melamed, Y., Szor, H., & Bernstein, E. (2001). The loneliness of the therapist in the public outpatient clinic. *Journal of Contemporary Psychotherapy, 31*(2), 103–112.

Miller, B. (2007). Innovations: Psychotherapy: What creates and sustains commitment to the practice of psychotherapy?. *Psychiatric Services, 58*(2), 174–176.

Rabke, E. (May 12, 2017). *A surprising cure for burnout*. Retrieved from https://embodimentmatters.com/a-surprising-cure-for-burnout/.

Schofield, W. (1964). *Psychotherapy: The purchase of friendship*. Englewood Cliffs, New Jersey: Prentice Hall.

Wharton, A. S. (2009). The sociology of emotional labor. *Annual Review of Sociology, 35*, 147–165.

Wilkinson, C. B., Infantolino, Z. P., & Wacha-Montes, A. (2017). Evidence-based practice as a potential solution to burnout in university counseling center clinicians. *Psychological Services, 14*(4), 543–548.

8 Breathing Lessons: Skills for Activating Parasympathetic Recovery

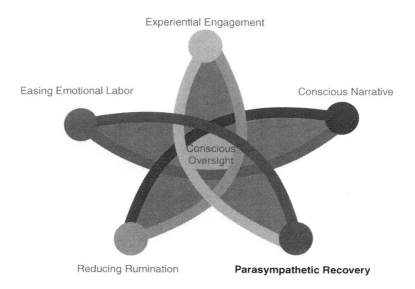

Incline toward your own distress as a mother would towards a distressed child.

Lynne Henderson (2019)

This—the third act—is the story of us "coming home". Our goal is to recover from the journey, the battles. Here I describe strategies for creating a sense of enough space that we can breathe during each day. I am continuing the theme of increasing the sense of ease during your workday. Already, that idea suggests the possibility of increased ease: *you are trying hard enough already*. Take a moment to relax into that: you are trying hard enough. You don't have to try harder to find the proper balance between work and life—or work harder in any other way.

The CE-CERT model can be portrayed as a series of lessons in how to breathe. All of the CE-CERT concepts and skills relate to either the inbreath or the outbreath—in the literal sense, but also, in the figurative—cognitive—sense. Each inbreath activates the sympathetic nervous system. Each outbreath activates recovery, the parasympathetic nervous system. Successful management of secondary trauma allows the waves of inbreath and outbreath to continue without mental interruption.

I supervised a child therapist who attached a green wooden square by the side of her office door. One day I asked her about her plaque, and she told me, "Oh—I have that there as a reminder. Each day when I leave the office, I put my hand on that plaque and say to myself, 'It stays here…'" That green plaque was, she explained, a reminder to leave the stress of work at the office, so she doesn't carry it home. I didn't say this to her—but I did think it: "And do you have a round red one by the front door of your home? And, when you leave home in the morning, do you say to yourself, 'All peace and happiness stays here'?"

I'm not critical of her idea; I understand it completely. But I believe that—in the figurative sense—she does indeed have that round red plaque at her home. Because this dynamic of opposites is the way our brain operates. She didn't intend to have the second plaque, only the one about leaving the stress behind. But—in her well-intended desire to not carry work stress home, she has inadvertently created its opposite dynamic—nothing from work comes home, nothing from home goes to work.

How about you? Have you ever set a goal of "leaving work at work"? Perhaps you have even been advised by supervisors, peers, or your partner that you should do just that, "leave work at work". In this book, I have emphasized how important it is that you believe deeply that your work is meaningful. And so, let me ask you a second question rhetorically: "Is your work of such little consequence you just want to leave it at the office?"

Of course, that isn't what you intend when you establish the goal of leaving "work at work". What you are trying to do—and what this child therapist was trying to do—is to leave the *stress* at the office. I don't fault her for that, and I don't fault you for that. But allow me to ask another provocative question that introduces the thesis of this chapter: why did you wait until 5:00 to try to resolve your stress?

A truism: sometimes your work is very hard. Sometimes it is unpleasant. And—another truism—sometimes it is fun and enjoyable. Now, if I fill this chapter with enough painfully obvious statements, I will have to re-name this chapter "No Kidding, Sherlock". But turn those statements inside out with an equally obvious observation: "Sometimes my evenings at home are relaxing and restorative. But sometimes, my evenings are just as stressful as work". I haven't met the person who could truthfully argue with either of those statements. They are true to a painfully obvious degree. Statement of the obvious but rarely stated: Sometimes your work isn't stressful, and sometimes your time at home is.

Now ask yourself something less obvious: does your narrative about your work comport with this simple reality? Does your work narrative allow for the up-and-down nature of your days? And does your narrative about your off-work time allow for the fun and relaxation, but also the stressful and boring periods that are part of that time? Or does your narrative assign a categorical valence to both work and life that looks like this: work = stress and emotional labor; leisure = relaxation and pleasure?

Ending the Search for Work–Life Balance

We count down the days: Blue Monday, Wednesday Hump Day, Thank-God-it's-Friday, until our "life" begins on Friday evening when we can leave work. That we have those clichés at all demonstrates how we mark time based on our hallowed weekends—how many days since or until the weekend. Unfortunately, lost in that attribution are the many moments of meaning and pleasure that were contained in that work week. We lose to experience and to memory the many moments of calm, of reward, and pleasure because of that unnuanced view that work = stress, being away from work = life.

The resolution of secondary traumatic stress or burnout is NOT to be found in creating a "work–life balance". "A master in the art of living draws no sharp distinction between his work and his play; his labor and his leisure", according to L.P. Jacks (Bryant, 2002). We have been led astray with this notion of "balance" because reducing time in one domain results in opportunity costs in the other domain. Now I will extend that argument even further with a provocation: *not only will you never find that elusive balance between work and life, but the harder you struggle for it, the worse the sense of imbalance will become.*

Here's what I noticed in my own experience: the only time I ever felt the magic of "I finally think I found the perfect balance between my work and the other parts of my life" was—suspiciously—Friday night after the second glass of wine. And, notably, that sense of balance was gone by Monday morning. Now I realize that it is always to be so.

Closely examine that notion of work–life balance, and you will see that the logic quickly falls apart. First, the division between work and "life": this categorization already corrupts the value of work—your work isn't even part of your "life"? And yet you spend 40 hours (50? 60?) of your precious time each week at work. That's a large chunk of your life. And, as I have underscored repeatedly by now, it is critical that we find ways of connecting our work to deep, personal meaning. We want our vocation to be seamlessly integrated *into* our life, not categorically dismissed from it.

The concept of "balance" has no basis in the physiological reality of stress. Stress is a demand placed on the body and psyche within a dynamic environment. It rises like a wave (sometimes a tsunami), and it fades away. Sometimes the demands placed upon us by our work are at near-crisis levels, and sometimes the demands recede and become less intense. There is no reasonable way you can establish a durable and sustainable "balance". It isn't about balance at all, or any other noun for that matter. In an ever-changing, dynamic environment, we need an action verb, not a noun: We must be able to manage the daily demands placed on us by *rebalancing*, not by establishing a "balance".

Another thought experiment: You have signed up for a weekend yoga class. As the class begins, the instructor has you assume savasana, or corpse pose. This pose is so named because it is completely effortless. You simply lie flat on your back with your arms and legs spread away from the body and begin scanning the body for any tension. When you notice tension, you tense and release that muscle as you remain in the pose. Savasana is the final, relaxing pose in the yoga session. It is an easy, nearly effortless pose.

In this thought experiment, however, a long time passes, and your instructor gives no further instruction. You note that, as the time passes, the instructor moves from one student to another gently moving a leg or arm but does not give any indication that you should move into another pose. As your boredom grows, you recall the flier that you saw that led to signing up for this class. And then it hits you: this is an advanced savasana class: you will spend the entire six-hour course in this position. If you are like me, you will feel stressed out at the thought of lying motionless and doing next-to-nothing all day. Indeed, in studies, people will prefer to administer painful electric shocks to themselves rather than simply being left alone with their thoughts with no other stimulation (Wilson et al., 2014).

On the other hand, if you were asked to assume one of the most strenuous poses—the crow pose, in which you are upside down supporting yourself with your hands tucked inside your knees—you couldn't tolerate holding this pose all day long. Yoga, of course, does not require one strenuous pose held for six hours, or for even one-half hour. Nor does it require that you remain in an effortless state on a mat for six hours. Yoga is, rather, about moving from high-effort to low-effort. From tension to release. Strenuous effort followed by recovery. This alternation is what comprises yoga. *And your job is the same.* Your workday isn't eight or more hours of "crow pose" in which you are straining to the full limits of your tolerance. Nor is your job eight hours of savasana—with low demand and low effort.

And, of course, you don't want your workday to be either maximum strain or maximum boredom (although sometimes a day or two of just lying on that mat with no demands sounds pretty good). I have good news for you—your job isn't one of those two things. It already is comprised of high-effort and low-effort tasks (and lots of medium-effort tasks). But when you make hard divisions between work and life, you fail to account for this obvious fact.

It may be the most controversial concept that I promote in CE-CERT when I suggest that you should abandon the work–life division. Many trauma workers cling to this concept as if it is a lifeline. I wouldn't challenge the concept if there was any evidence that it helped sustain a career in trauma work. But thinking in these black-and-white terms does more harm than good.

Maybe if we agree about some things upfront it will lessen any resistance you may have to the idea that we should give up the work–life balance notion. Agreement #1: We want to seek balance in the time and energy that we put into work with the time and energy that we put into recreation, family, and home tasks. Of course, we do. Agreement #2: We sometimes need to give ourselves permission to leave the office because we prioritize something else, or we will stay too long. Agreement #3: Undisputedly, we don't want to carry the stress of a high-demand job home into the rest of our relationships and time.

All three of those statements are true and are worthy goals. Seeking these aims is what leads us to segment our life into categories relating to "work" and "life". But these worthy goals are not best served by developing hard boundaries between these parts of our life. When you think of your time allocation in those terms, it is human nature to play them off from each other and assign one a positive valence and one a negative valence. Especially when we are feeling time pressure and job stress. "Work" doesn't stand a chance in this competition. Once you have assigned your job the label "stressful", you will naturally begin to smear your reality with that valence. You will begin to assume a defensive crouch as you start the day and try to hold on each day until 5:00 PM and hold on from Monday morning until Friday evening. Work is unpleasant; "life" is pleasant. Work is for the benefit of the organization; "life" is for my own benefit.

You begin to approach your job with what Ben-Shahar (2007) terms the "drowning model" of happiness. That is, you postpone any expectation of enjoyment as you hold your breath waiting for Friday evening. Friday at 5:00, your lungs ready to burst, you can break the surface of the water and take a big breath. And it feels so good, because you have been holding your breath all week long waiting for this moment. Many of us got through our graduate training using this drowning model—holding our breath, denying ourselves many pleasures. We focused on studying and thinking about how great it was going to feel when we once again came up for air. When we allowed our head to break the surface of the water, graduate diploma and professional license in hand, we once again could enjoy life.

When you approach your work with this drowning strategy—trying to hold on until the end of the day, end of the week, or next vacation, we blind ourselves to the many pleasant, rewarding moments that happened during the workday. There is an important concept here: *the more we segment the hours of our day into categories, the less time it seems we have.* If we segment our days according to work time and "me" time, stress time and play time, the kid's time and my time, we will never have a sense of space. It will seem that we never have enough time for ourselves because we are giving so much of it away—often with resentment.

And—at both the psychological and physiological level this breath-holding waiting for "my time" keeps us in a state of low-level fight or flight (sympathetic response) all week long. Instead of stress event followed by recovery, stress event/recovery; we are in a cycle of constant stress punctuated by acute stress; back to constant stress/acute stress. We never fully recover. We tell ourselves that we will recover in the evenings or weekends, but that may not be the case either.

If you have to choose, which ONE statement best represents your physiological state while at work: 1) calm; 2) fight; 3) flight; 4) freeze. Of course, you know that the accurate answer to that question is "all of the above", but don't allow yourself that choice. The narrative that you maintain—if that narrative is about work–life balance—won't allow you to choose more than one.

That is why we need breathing lessons. We need to learn to breathe all day long, all week long. We need to attend to our stress in real time all day long. We need to note the calm, enjoyable, and rewarding moments that we are having throughout the workweek. We need to experience the whitespace that exists in-between the stress events. That points us toward paying more attention to parasympathetic recovery.

Parasympathetic Recovery

You already know the sympathetic nervous system. This system activates fight or flight when we are under stress. The stress response begins with a release of adrenaline and other hormones that results in an increase in heart rate, blood pressure, and breathing rate. After the acute stress has resolved, it takes about 20–60 minutes for the body to return to a state of homeostasis.

The system that creates recovery from the activation of the sympathetic nervous system is the parasympathetic system. In contrast to fight or flight, the parasympathetic system is sometimes termed the "rest and digest system". We tend to emphasize the sympathetic response when we talk about stress. We don't often address parasympathetic recovery, which directs recovery from stress. This system is the part of the autonomic nervous system that operates directly to turn off the fight-or-flight response.

Two things to consider about parasympathetic recovery: 1) Parasympathetic recovery is initiated by a signal that the acute stressor is over. Therefore—in order for this recovery mechanism to do its work—we have to *notice* that the stress is over. 2) Only when we are in recovery can concern for others—compassion—be activated. During the sympathetic response, we necessarily move our focus to our own well-being—physical and emotional. So, the goal of being the compassionate therapists to which we aspire depends on us having a toned parasympathetic response.

Understanding the moment-by-moment relationship of the sympathetic (fight or flight) and parasympathetic (rest and digest) systems allows us to view our days in a more nuanced way than does the "work–life" schema. All day long we are moving from one system—sympathetic—to the other—parasympathetic. Deliberately moving between these mechanisms is cognitive breathing. And, as I said in the introduction to this chapter, the actual breath is cuing one system (inbreath = sympathetic) or the other (outbreath = parasympathetic). This is the natural rhythm of our day, and we don't want to interrupt those waves. Rather, we want to notice the rises and falls of these waves, allow them, and avoid interrupting this natural process. We want to breathe all day long, not hold our breath until we can get home and begin to breathe.

I was happy recently to find support for the idea of giving up our goal of work–life balance from none other than Jeff Bezos, CEO of Amazon. I think he says it very well: "It actually is a circle. It's not a balance. If I am happy at home, I come into the office with tremendous energy", said Bezos. "And if I am happy at work, I come home with tremendous energy" (Bernard, 2019).

Certainly, reducing the amount of emotional labor required by each workday (Chapter 5) greatly facilitates this circle. Now we add more to that formula: 1) softening the boundaries between work and the rest of our life; and 2) breathing while we are at work.

You do not want to carry the stress of a difficult day home to pollute your evening activities and relationships. But you also don't want to hang that plaque by the front door of your home that removes any expectation of rest and joy from your workday. Creating the circle that Jeff Bezos describes requires that we soften those work–life boundaries so that we can do both of these things—resolve our workplace stress so we don't carry it home, and open up to the many positive moments we have during work.

Bridging Concepts to Skills—Skills for Cognitive Breathing

Setting the Target

The targets for this skill domain—parasympathetic recovery—are two: 1) Recognizing when we have moved out of the "green zone" and employing a real-time, active strategy for recovery. This target allows for the natural "waves" of stress activation and stress recovery that comprise cognitive breathing; and 2) Creating a sense of space during the workday in which recovery occurs naturally and repeatedly throughout the day. The first target is very deliberate and active, the second target is about creating a surrounding environment in which cognitive breathing/stress recovery becomes natural and automatic.

Practice in Your Practice

The focus of parasympathetic recovery is real-time recovery from stress events. Creation of the circle instead of the "balance" dynamic happens when we revise the narrative that the day's work is all stress, followed by recovery in the evening. Instead of that narrative, we will shift to a model in which we continuously: 1) notice and allow stressors—the inbreath or rise of the wave, followed by 2) parasympathetic recovery—the outbreath or falling of the wave.

I am fond of the phrase "practice in your practice". The idea of practicing in your practice helps make a distinction from the work–life balance paradigm. The CE-CERT acronym includes the concept "enhancing clinician experience". Enhancing your experience is a practice done in real time, not when you get home from work. Practicing in your practice indicates that you are practicing parasympathetic recovery skills as you practice your trauma treatment skills. You are applying these practices all day long as the waves rise and fall.

Conscious Oversight

The poet Rumi asked us to consider if we make regular visits to ourselves. More concretely—during your workday—are you aware of the effect that stress is having on you emotionally and physiologically? Are you aware of these effects as they happen, or only later as they accumulate? If you are like most therapists, I fear that your answer is that you only become aware of it later. We therapists have a tendency to—and even have been trained to—dereflect from our feelings because we are focusing so intently on our client's feelings or upon the resolution of any given situation. But the metabolization of feelings requires that we recognize those feelings. We need the "luxury" of knowing that we are stressed when we are stressed. This helps us better engage those feelings, but also supports our active efforts at releasing the stress when the time is right.

Without knowing anything about your role or your organization, I can confidently state that your day contains stressful *situations* (a difficult client) as well as stress-engendering *conditions* (conflict with supervisors), but there are also edges to the stress conditions. There are moments in which the stress factors are low. There are moments in which you are interacting with colleagues whom you like. The ocean of stress of your experience is created when you smear your stress valence over the entirety of the day. Or you forget to breathe—inhaling to activate fight or flight but failing to recover before the next stressor. If you don't notice the edges that define the stress events, it all feels like one constant stress. But that sense of constant stress isn't based in reality.

Acknowledge Distress

Regardless of your gender or sex, as a trauma worker you have probably received a message that you should "cowboy up" for this kind of work. The cowboy ethic is to show no vulnerability. You are implicitly—if not explicitly—expected to be unaffected by difficult clients, tragic images, and high job demands. I advise that this expectation be explicitly changed.

This focus of this chapter is resolving stress in real time. In order for you to resolve stress, you need to both notice and acknowledge that stress. Begin by admitting discomfort to yourself, whether it is mild or substantial. Certainly, it is preferable if this acknowledgement of distress is allowed and encouraged within the organizational culture—but if not—allow it within yourself.

The next time after you've had something stressful happen, and someone asks you how you are doing, truly query yourself. You know the expected script: "No, I'm fine". Don't blindly follow that script. *Really* ask yourself, "What am I feeling?" And allow yourself—silently or out loud—to acknowledge what is true. "Yes, I'm really upset right now..." In the cognitive breathing context, this also implicitly communicates—to yourself and others— "...but I won't be upset later". That is how the edges are defined.

Note my use of the term "stress event". Stress is an *event* that is caused by an occurrence with a discrete episode with a beginning and an end. These experiences have edges that we must begin to notice. This distinction of an "event"—rather than a condition—suggests the cognitive breath. Stress comes, and stress goes. Inbreath and outbreath. This contrasts with the way we typically talk about stress, "My job is very stressful". Viewing stress this way suggests that each day you dive into the ocean of stress that is your job. And that view—that your work is an unending ocean of stress—requires the very breath-holding that we are seeking to modify.

Chuck Pyle was a folk-country singer who was known as the "Zen Cowboy". That's the only kind of "cowboying up" that we should try for—the "Zen" kind. The Zen Cowboy ethic is to notice and acknowledge feelings—that's the Zen—with confidence that you will not be swamped by those feelings—that's the Cowboy. Soft front. Strong back.

Many trauma-exposed workplaces have a culture of "that's what we signed up for—buck up, Buttercup". And certainly, that same thinking becomes internalized. We may not acknowledge, even to ourselves, that certain situations were stressful or difficult. But we can't breathe out—recover from stress—unless we have breathed in fully. Breathing in is the acknowledgement of stress. Instead of holding our breath until the end of the day, learn how to breathe.

Mindfulness of Body

When you make that visit to yourself—or when your co-worker asks you if you are okay—that can be your cue to become mindful of your body. If you aren't sure what you are feeling, becoming aware of your physical sensations will tell you. I think of the Cat Stevens/Yusuf Islam lyric in which the young man decries his father, "...from the moment I could talk, I was ordered to listen...". That renunciation is coming from your body as well. Because you have been cowboying on, you have learned to ignore what your body is telling you. "From the moment you started this job", your body is saying, "I have been trying to talk, but you ordered me to listen...". Becoming mindful by dropping back into your body allows your body to talk. Your body will tell you how you are doing.

Dropping Anchor

You have just experienced some stress event. The situation itself has ended, but you are still experiencing stress. There is that default mode again, recreating the stress experience and keeping our stress alive well after the event is over. It is time to come back home. You had to leave awareness of your body as you moved into fight or flight—that's okay; you did just exactly what you should have done during a stressful experience. Now you can come back into your body again. Recognize that the situation has ended. Acknowledge that it was difficult and that you are stressed. Now, however, you have shelter over your head. You are safe. Sit down. Let yourself come back to yourself.

If you just do the first thing—note the stress and when it is finished—you are already changing the pattern of your breathing. If you do that much, you probably already know what to do next. When the waters are choppy, how do you drop anchor? If you are like most of us, you have some answers (breathing strategies, mindfulness meditation, etc.) but you don't do them on a daily basis ("I'm way too busy!"). You have just breathed in by opening up to a stress event. Now—by acknowledging the stress and the end of the event—you have completed the inbreath. Now comes the exhale. Any strategy that helps you "re-embody" will work as the exhalation: breath awareness, mindfulness exercise, brief walk, whatever you prefer. The goal is to return to a feeling of being back in your body.

I discovered—and personally like—the "two-feet-one-breath" exercise in published research on mindfulness strategies for physicians. This less-than-a-minute practice consists of simply taking a pause to become mindful of the weight on your feet as you stand—noting your weight on your two feet. Then, mindfully following one breath cycle—one breath. Dr. Luke Fortney had physicians employ "practice in your practice" strategies such as this two-feet-one-breath as part of an investigation into the effectiveness of an abbreviated mindfulness-based stress reduction program designed for busy physicians. He asked physicians to employ the two-feet-one-breath strategy each time before they entered an exam room. As a result of this abbreviated stress-reduction program, Fortney and his colleagues were able to demonstrate significant reductions in levels of depression, burnout, anxiety, and distress in those physicians (Fortney et al., 2013). I find the two-feet-one-breath practice to be a quick way of restoring awareness of the body after being harried or stressed.

Creating Whitespace

Softening the boundaries between work and life cannot occur if each workday begins with a sense that you are stepping onto the treadmill that will push you to your limit until the end of the day. We won't experience a soft transition from home to work if each workday begins with a sense of dread. We must be able to trust and confidently predict that we will have some breathing room during the workday—and we must have lived experiences of this whitespace. Then, instead of preparing to hold your breath all day, you become confident that you are going to cognitively breathe throughout the day. You don't have to take that deep inhale before you dive in. That may require some re-engineering—of your day, as well as your perceptions.

I was consulting with a women's advocacy organization when one of the case managers recounted one day the previous week she came home with abdominal pain. It was only then that she realized that the pain was because she hadn't had time to go to the bathroom all day. That has to represent the exact opposite of whitespace in your day. Who wouldn't divide their life into work and life under such unrelenting pressure? Who wouldn't long for five o'clock when "life" can begin? Working under this kind of relentless pressure requires that you remain in fight or flight all day long.

But, as we deconstructed her sense of a complete lack of space, we found—as I often do—that this pressure wasn't entirely the organization's creation (senior managers were part of this problem solving and were shocked to hear her sense of their expectations). Nor was this woman entirely creating this expectation. She was a self-described perfectionist, to be sure, but the practice of being available to clients non-stop for your entire shift was the cultural norm amongst the case management team.

If you want a fire to burn hot, you have to have some space between the logs—you cannot just keep jamming more and more wood into it. When it comes to your workday, you also have to create space between the logs. In my experience, you almost certainly have more degrees of freedom to engineer space into your workday than you have realized. It simply requires recognition of the importance of this space and an unswerving commitment to make it so. In some cases, taking space may require that you buck some cultural norms. This effort will require that you give permission to yourself to allow some moments to breathe. The strategies that I will list in this skill domain—five minutes of movement each hour, taking lunch out of the office, team support—are examples of this whitespace:

Five Minutes of Movement Each Hour

Francesco Cirillo (n.d.) has, since the late 1980s, advocated a time management strategy that he termed the "pomodoro method". The pomodoro method is a strategy of dividing your work into 25-minute "pomodoros" in which you focus intently and work efficiently, followed by a five-minute break to exercise, make a cup of coffee, meditate, or engage in any non-work activity. After four pomodoros, you take a longer 15- or 20-minute break. I wrote this book using this method, and it works for me. The clinical hour does not allow for 25-minute "pomodoros", nor am I advocating specifically for this method. Rather, I offer the pomodoro method as an example of intentionally creating cognitive breaths—25 minutes of inbreath, followed by scheduled outbreaths. This same principle suggests that after a 50-minute clinical session, you should build into your routine a deliberate outbreath.

I recommend—and there is research to support—the value of five minutes of movement each hour. Bergouignan and colleagues demonstrated that five minutes of walking each hour increases worker happiness and energy and reduced food cravings (Bergouignan et al., 2016). I am focusing on the value of the deliberate cognitive exhale. After each inbreath—the 50-minute clinical hour—remember to take the five-minute outbreath—five minutes of movement. That there are additional benefits only strengthens the case for building this into your routine.

I know, I know—you don't have time for a five-minute walk each hour. When I hear someone say this—or when I feel the same time pressure—I offer a mindfulness teacher's response to one of his students. The student resisted his call to do 20 minutes of meditation each day, saying he was simply too busy. The mindfulness teacher's answer? "Oh, if you are that busy, you need two 20-minute meditation sessions each day". Take his point. I have worked many years in behavioral health and physical healthcare settings. I certainly realize that these settings may not readily be conducive to taking a five-minute walk each hour (or doing deep knee bends or meditation or whatever you would choose). That is precisely why you must take deliberate action, and even take an action that may violate the cultural norm of your office. Your physical and emotional health are that important.

Support from Team

When you consider the concept of "parasympathetic recovery", your mind might naturally go to strategies such as meditation or yoga. But it is very likely that you are already employing a highly effective strategy for creating recovery. And you do it multiple times each day. That is, you seek or accept the shared experience and support of your colleagues. When we are engaged in a social exchange with a trusted other, parasympathetic response is in full activation.

Ever since Cannon coined the concept of fight or flight in 1915, the stress response has been described as resulting in one of those two options, fight or flight. Often—including in this book—we add a third option: freezing. All of these responses—fight, flight, or freeze—are efforts to deal with the stressor. Either by ending the source of the stress (fighting) or by getting away from it (fleeing or freezing). But humans—being the tribal/social creatures that we are—have another important way of contending with stress challenges: we pull into social groups. At a deep level, we feel safest when we are with other people whom we trust. It is easy to infer the evolutionary origins of this response: out there, alone amongst the dangers, we feel threatened. Back with our tribe of trusted others, we feel safe. The soothing/calming system has evolved over 120 million years in order to quiet the fight-or-flight response. Feeling isolated is the biggest single risk factor to stress exposure. Conversely, feeling connected to others is the single most important protective factor.

If you startle from an unexpected, loud noise, you are likely to do something even before you fight or flee: you will look around at anyone you are with to read the social cues about whether that was something you should be concerned about, or whether you should just proceed with whatever you were doing. In other words, we social animals—in addition to fighting or fleeing—tend to cue from—and gather into—social groups. In keeping with the "f" themes of the fight-or-flight response, I call this flocking. We gather together because we feel safer with someone than by ourselves when we are under stress. But this "flocking" doesn't have to be a big group. An interaction with one other person will cue parasympathetic recovery.

I suggested this same strategy of engaging with another person as an intentional way of reducing rumination in Chapter 3. I offer the strategy again here as a way of inducing the cognitive outbreath. Being engaged in conversation with a trusted other has been shown to activate the vagal nerve, resulting in parasympathetic recovery and a return to the emotional "green zone".

What am I advising here is that you begin to do with deliberateness something that you already do naturally—to seek out a conversation with another person after you have experienced some small or significant stressor. It is a given is that you will be respectful of the time of your colleagues. But as a principle, think of this as a five-minute exchange with a colleague when you experience the need for an outbreath.

This moment of connecting with a co-worker is when you begin constructing your consolidation narrative, turning dysregulation into a coherent narrative. The act of describing the experience and its effect upon you allows it to move through you. As does the experience of sharing it with another. And—I hope it goes without saying—you are equally willing to play the same role for them. And when you do, your role is to listen with curiosity and mindfulness. The reciprocal nature of the human relationship is such that this shared exchange activates parasympathetic recovery not only for them, but in you as well.

There is further benefit from these interpersonal connections when we notice and savor them. As we recalibrate our strategy these connections help us open up to the day, so we don't begin breath-holding. We can guide our narratives towards gentle reminders that our goal is not to set our jaw so that we can muscle it through our day. Our goal is not to hold our breath and to try to be immovable in the face of any stressor. It is, rather to feel rooted enough that we allow ourselves to sway as the stressors come and go. To do this, you must *believe* that you are firmly rooted—that you possess a "strong back". We can do that by constantly bathing in the knowledge that we are doing this work among a team of trusted others.

In a calm moment, do a quick analysis of your typical workday. What percentage of your time will be spent in a high-stress activity? What portion will be spent in low-level stress activity? Neutral or monotonous activities? And—don't forget this one—what percentage of your time will be spent in pleasant activities? Specifically, during how much of your day will you be in pleasant interactions with your colleagues and with your clients? During those moments of pleasant, non-conflictual exchanges, you are in parasympathetic recovery. These are you moments in which you take the outbreath. You are probably already doing this—but in your work–life balance schema, are you including these positive and restorative experiences? Are you noticing them as they occur?

It is a workday morning. When you notice yourself breathing in deeply—literally or figuratively—anticipating a long day, remind yourself that you will be breathing all day long. Remind yourself that you will sway with the stressful and with the calm moments. And that you are going to connect with clients and with colleagues. You don't have to take that deep breath, because you don't have to hold your breath today.

Kate Braestrup, a law enforcement chaplain, was quoted by Krista Tippet (2016) making a relevant point: "You know, the question isn't are we going to do hard, awful things, because we are. We all are. The question is are we going to have to do them alone?" Trauma treatment is, as I have said in multiple contexts, emotionally difficult work. It is important that you have a sense of doing it as a team member, and not as a lone wolf.

I have a phrase I use almost as a mantra in clinical supervision: "Here, each difficult case is held by each of us and by all of us..." This feeling of being on a team—of being amongst our own—brings about para-sympathetic recovery. We aren't holding these difficult cases alone. They are—on a healthy team at least—being held by all of us.

You socialize with your co-workers because you are bored, because you root for the same sports team, because you want to debrief a difficult session. Perhaps you need to do it even more. Or—more likely—you need to socialize with increased deliberateness: with the realization that this represents the cognitive exhale.

The anthropologist Clifford Geertz said that "the work of culture is to make suffering bearable" (1973). The work of teams is to make stress bearable. Noticing this makes it easier tomorrow to trust our cognitive breath and not to be inclined to hold our breath as we begin our workday.

Lunchtime

As we lay out strategies for facilitating the cognitive breath, I am obligated to point to the most obvious opportunity for you to take a deep exhale: lunchtime. For most of you, a lunch hour is already built into the workflow of your organization. But do you fully capitalize on the potential benefit of this opportunity for a mid-day breath? Do you remain at your desk? Do you eat alone while on the computer? Do you take a full lunch break at all? No less a source than saddesklunch.com reports that 62% of us eat lunch sitting at the same desk we have been working at all day. That comports with my experience in the trauma treatment field. I know many trauma workers that go for weeks or months without taking a lunch break at all. In some organizations, it is the cultural norm to remain at your desk, catching up on emails and documentation.

I anticipate that some of you are saying to yourself, "He doesn't know how crazy it is where I work". "He doesn't know how busy I am". I don't know your role or your organization's demands. But I know how important it is to take time to exhale. I deliberately used the term "take time" as opposed to "have time". You probably don't have time to take a full lunch break each day. But will you *take* time? Will you prioritize your long-term well-being and the sustainability of your role?

Begin by seeing the vision: After a busy morning in which you were scrambling to do two things at once, dealing with stressful clients with complex needs, and unending organizational demands, twelve o'clock arrives. You—because we are creating the ideal vision—make a clean break from work demands. You meet a friend at a restaurant. Maybe the restaurant is within walking distance from your office. But, even if not, you get a little walking in as you move from your office to your car and from the car to the restaurant. You get a few minutes of sunshine as you walk outside. You get a little non-work socialization with your friend. You eat a delicious and nutritious meal. And then you return to the office.

Before you push back with "Come on, get real here—as if I'm going to do that every day", I want you to catch the vision of how refreshed you will feel as you begin the final half of your day. Contrast that with the "sad desk lunch"—the most vivid example I saw on the saddesklunch site was a man who sat at his desk eating a leftover hotdog bun stuffed with chips and pretzels and slathered in hot sauce that he had scavenged from the office breakroom. Credit that poor soul with resourcefulness if not good nutrition. But it is a pathetically sad desk lunch.

I don't know the limits of what you can—or will—do in regard to your lunch break. Certainly, I understand that it will not always be the idyll that I described, with a friend and at a nice restaurant. But lunchtime creates a supreme opportunity to exhale fully—right in the middle of the workday. A brownbag lunch under a tree may do the trick also. And the more often you can do that, the easier it will be to come in to work each day without feeling like you have to take a deep breath and hold it before you plunge into those icy waters.

"Time is an illusion", said the author Douglas Adams, "Lunchtime doubly so…"

End-of-Workday Soft Transition

I began this chapter with a description of the unintended effects of seeking that elusive work–life balance. But—although I made an argument against segmenting our life into hard boundaries between work and home—it is true some of us may need strategies for making a soft transition from work. You may need a clear signal that your attention can shift from work to the rest of your day. Many of us take a deep inbreath as we scramble to tie things up before we leave for the day. Then, we take a deep inbreath considering what we have to do tomorrow, and what we have to do to get the kids ready for dinner, homework, bedtime. In other words, we keep taking inbreaths—but we don't exhale.

By "soft transition" I am referring to the creation of a routine that isn't an abrupt swerve from work mode to home mode—but does, at the same time, support your changing of roles. We need to take an outbreath to finish the day and ease into the evening. We want to carry the feeling of accomplishing something meaningful home. But we don't want to carry a sense of pressure and time shortage home.

Daniel Pink, in his book *When: The Scientific Secrets of Perfect Timing* (2018), describes an end-of-day transition that I find to be consistent with the CE-CERT approach to soft transitions. The ritual itself can serve as a signal for you to wrap things up so you give yourself permission to call it a day. Pink suggests a five-minute ritual and the end of the workday that consists of three, two- to- three minute practices:

Write a list of what you accomplished today (2–3 minutes).

In CE-CERT terms, this list develops a narrative that you are accomplishing things—and it reminds you that some of these things are meaningful. This practice also does what narratives do: it puts the day properly in the "past" file so you don't carry a sense of unfinished business forward. And—if you are like me—when you do this practice of reviewing your day, you will often discover that you have more items on your accomplished list than you *feel* like you did. I find that even on days in which I felt very unfocused and ineffective, my list is longer than I expected. That's a great note to end the day on.

Lay out your plan for tomorrow (2–3 minutes):

Undoubtedly, this is an effective time management strategy. Having this plan ready tomorrow morning will focus you. You don't have to take time to orient yourself by trying to remember where you left off yesterday. And it just might help delay you from going immediately to that siren song that we call the email inbox. Perhaps that is why Pink recommends this plan. But I recommend it from a CE-CERT perspective—listing tomorrow's plan is an active strategy for pinning down potential sources of evening rumination. Once you jot down those things you need to remember, you don't need to actively keep them in mind any longer. You can give yourself permission to focus your thoughts and energies toward home and evening activities. In the evening—or on the weekend—if you find yourself beginning to feel stress in anticipation of the next workday, you can remind yourself that the list is there waiting for you in the morning. You don't need to do anything in the meantime except focus in the present. You can redirect yourself from work rumination and re-engage in your evening activities.

Send thank-you notes (any remaining time):

You have seen the reports that gratitude practice elevates our mood and sense of well-being. But the CE-CERT dimension involved here is the parasympathetic effect when you experience the feeling that you are part of a team. This simple exercise is very effective at creating this sense of comradery. Simply shoot a quick email or two (or even an old-fashioned written thank-you note) to someone thanking them for something they did for you. If you try this exercise even once, you will undoubtedly note an immediate sense of improved well-being. And you will have a nice sense that you are making someone else's day, and that makes you a good colleague. That nice feeling that you are experiencing? That is the exhale of the cognitive breath. That's exactly the state that you want to be in before you head home.

Evening: At Least 20 Minutes "Returning to Tao"

One of the distinctive characteristics of CE-CERT is that it is a set of skills and practices that are applied to your work in *real time*. There is, however, one exception to the during worktime emphasis: making a practice of finding some absorbing activity that you can lose yourself in (literally lose your "self" in) for at least 20 minutes each evening.

Many observers have noted the poor fit between our sympathetic nervous system that evolved to deal with acute stress events, and the chronic nature of the stress field in which we labor. The fight-or-flight system evolved to improve our chances with the proverbial saber tooth tiger. But a big response preparing us for a rare life-and-death threat doesn't represent the stress with which we contend. Our stress is at a lower level of intensity but is also a more unrelenting type of stress. We don't contend with the saber tooth tiger, but rather, our days are filled with a number of "little murders" all day long.

In view of this poor fit, it is noteworthy how well most of us handle stress. We do well, that is, with one big if: *if we recover fully at some point each day*. Each time we fully recover from stress—full parasympathetic exhale—we reset to a lower register of arousal. Any stress event thereafter is experienced less severely because it isn't occurring on top of the whole day's accumulation of "little murders". Stress is most harmful when it is unrelenting—each stress adds more dysregulation to an already over-worked system.

I advocate for a full, 20-minute exhalation each evening as a way of returning fully to your resting baseline. There is something of a con-vergence that within that 15- to 30-minute window there are significant benefits to mood, energy, and stress resilience with different activities. Activities as varied as meditation (Basso et al., 2019); connecting with nature (Hunter et al., 2019); or physical exercise (Chan et al., 2019) produce tremendous benefit within this short amount of time. And there is no reason to believe that this is only true for activities that we typically put on the "stress reduction" list, such as yoga or meditation. Any ac-tivity in which you become deeply absorbed (needlepoint or pickleball anyone?) is likely to confer benefit. The only criterion is that you *com-pletely* recover from the dysregulation of the day. Only 20 minutes ty-pically is effective at restoring our state to a condition of "rest and digest".

The alternation of sympathetic arousal and parasympathetic recovery represents the cognitive breath. I speak of the cognitive breath as a me-taphor, but there is also a very material connection between our breath and the sympathetic and parasympathetic response. The goal of this chapter has been for us to change a basic premise: breathing happens when we *aren't* working, and during our workday we are free-diving into the depths, and we must hold our breath. But breathing during the day creates a sense of spaciousness. If I note the many easy moments that I have during the day, enjoy affiliating with people I like, and rely on having breathing room each day, then I am less inclined to tense up in defense against another workday.

Ultimately, if we do this well enough, we can even realize the secret Alan Watts (1977) described: "This is the real secret of life—to be completely engaged with what you are doing in the here and now. And instead of calling it work, realize it is play".

Breathing Lessons: Parasympathetic Recovery

You Must Remember This

- The goal of seeking balance between "work and life" inadvertently creates a tension between work and life. This split makes work seem more onerous.
- Effective stress management is a dynamic process of constant *rebalancing*, not arriving at balance. Dynamic rebalancing requires conscious oversight throughout the day in the form of "cognitive breathing".
- The parasympathetic nervous system is the part of the autonomic nervous system that turns off the fight-or-flight response. The cognitive breath refers to the sympathetic response (the inbreath) that occurs during a stress event, followed by the parasympathetic response (the outbreath) that resolves the arousal.
- If we fail to engage in "cognitive breathing" during the day because we are holding our breath waiting for the end of the day, stress events accumulate as one stress adds to the previous stress all day long. Stress is experienced as one continuous event all day long instead of waves that rise and fall.
- In order to activate the outbreath (parasympathetic recovery), we need to notice the "edges" of the stress event and note when the stressor has ended.
- Compassion toward our clients can only occur when we are in our emotional "green zone"; that is, we have parasympathetically recovered. Physiologically we are unable to experience compassion when we are in fight or flight.
- The goal of parasympathetic recovery is to allow the natural rise and fall of the stress response throughout the day without interruption.
- There are two targets with the parasympathetic recovery skills:

  - To improve our skillfulness in noticing our stress response and activating recovery
  - To create a sense of space during the day that provides openings to breathe

Bridging Concepts to Skills

1. *Conscious Oversight:* During your workday, develop deliberate awareness of the effect that stress is having on you emotionally and physiologically. Establish a goal of engaging in strategies deliberately to allow resolution of the fight-or-flight response after a stress event.
2. *Acknowledge Distress:* Stress is an *event.* We want to get better at defining the edges of the stress event—when it begins (inbreath,

acknowledging the stress) and when it ends (the outbreath, notice the stress has ended).

3. *Mindfulness of Body:* Part of the practice of conscious oversight is occasionally dropping back into your body—what sensations do you notice? Are you experiencing unacknowledged stress? Are you in a calm moment of exhalation? Your body will tell you.

4. *Dropping Anchor:* When we note that we are in the aftermath of a stress event, but we still feel some amount of stress reactivity, we need to intentionally employ a strategy to hold our place in the choppy waters. Dropping anchor strategies are actions that you already know and may already be employing such as breathing strategies, mindfulness meditation, or taking a walk. Any strategy that helps you emotionally and physically return to a calm state creates the exhalation after the stress.

5. *Creating Whitespace:* Creating whitespace between the stressful moments allows you to recover from each and every stress, rather than experiencing your day as one constant stress. Creating such whitespace may require some re-engineering—of your day, as well as reworking your perceptions about your day to a heightened aware-ness of what is really happening.

6. *Five minutes of movement each hour:* Build a deliberate outbreath into your routine. Research supports the value of five minutes of physical movement each hour.

7. *Support from Team:* One of the largest threats of stress exposure occurs when we experience that stress in solitude. Conversely, the single most protective factor for stress exposure is social connected-ness. This well-established fact about the importance of social connectedness leads to three strategies to increase stress resilience: the goal is not only to have these moments of pleasant social exchange, but we acknowledge them and their effect on us.

8. *Lunchtime:* Effective use of this time—ideally including some move-ment, mindful eating, and socialization—can allow for a complete outbreath before entering the second half of the workday.

9. *End-of-Workday Soft Transition:* The transition serves to solidify the meaning of the work that day, but at the same time help us to resolve any remaining dysregulation before we leave the office.

10. *At Least 20 Minutes of "Returning to Tao":* Any activity in which you become deeply absorbed, and that you enjoy, is likely to confer benefit. The goal is to get a complete "reboot" each day.

Breathing Lessons: Parasympathetic Recovery

Self-Audit

1. I feel that I seamlessly transition from home to work and vice versa.

0	1	2	3	4	5		6	7	8	9	10
Never					Sometimes		Always				

2. I have enough breathing room in my day—or enough pleasant activities—that I am able to maintain my emotion regulation at work.

0	1	2	3	4	5		6	7	8	9	10
Never					Sometimes		Always				

3. I have a set of "go-to" strategies I turn to during the workday when I'm feeling stressed out.

0	1	2	3	4	5		6	7	8	9	10
Never					Sometimes		Always				

4. I feel like my workplace team shares the weight of difficult situations that I encounter—I'm not dealing with everything by myself.

0	1	2	3	4	5		6	7	8	9	10
Never					Sometimes		Always				

5. I am in the "green zone" state of calmness when I leave for work and when I arrive home.

0	1	2	3	4	5		6	7	8	9	10
Never					Sometimes		Always				

6. My work stress feels like it is caused by specific events (as opposed to a constant state).

0	1	2	3	4	5		6	7	8	9	10
Never					Sometimes						

Your Parasympathetic Gauge

Descriptive Statements

Gray	I don't have to "take a deep breath" before I begin work. I have as much recovery time built into my workdays as I do stressors.
Light Gray	I often don't have time for lunch (even if I wanted to take a lunch break) and often don't have time to even think about how high my stress level is.
Black	I feel like I'm holding my breath all day until I get off work and can recover.

References

Basso, J. C., McHale, A., Ende, V., Oberlin, D. J., & Suzuki, W. A. (2019). Brief, daily meditation enhances attention, memory, mood, and emotional regulation in non-experienced meditators. *Behavioural Brain Research*, *356*, 208–220.

Ben-Shahar, T. (2007). *Happier: Learn the secrets to daily joy and lasting fulfillment*. New York: McGraw-Hill Companies.

Bergouignan, A., Legget, K. T., De Jong, N., Kealey, E., Nikolovski, J., Groppel, J. L., & Bessesen, D. H. (2016). Effect of frequent interruptions of prolonged sitting on self-perceived levels of energy, mood, food cravings and cognitive function. *International Journal of Behavioral Nutrition and Physical Activity*, *13*(1), 1–12.

Bernard, Z. (January 9, 2019). *Business insider.* Jeff Bezos' advice to Amazon employees is to stop aiming for work-life 'balance'—here's what you should strive for instead. Retrieved from https://www.businessinsider.com/jeff-bezo-advice-to-amazon-employees-dont-aim-for-work-life-balance-its-a-circle-2018-4.

Bryant, H. (2002). *Hallie's comet: Breaking the code: What successful people know and what others are trying to find out.* Detroit, MI: DTE Productions.

Chan, J. S., Liu, G., Liang, D., Deng, K., Wu, J., & Yan, J. H. (2019). Special issue–therapeutic benefits of physical activity for mood: A systematic review on the effects of exercise intensity, duration, and modality. *The Journal of Psychology*, *153*(1), 102–125.

Cirillo, F. (n.d.). *The pomodoro technique.* Retrieved December 11, 2020, from https://francescocirillo.com/pages/pomodoro-technique.

Fortney, L., Luchterhand, C., Zakletskaia, L., Zgierska, A., & Rakel, D. (2013). Abbreviated mindfulness intervention for job satisfaction, quality of life, and compassion in primary care clinicians: A pilot study. *The Annals of Family Medicine*, *11*(5), 412–420.

Geertz, Clifford. (1973). *The interpretation of cultures: Selected essays.* New York: Basic Books.

Henderson, L. (2019). *Improving social confidence and reducing shyness using compassion focused therapy.* London: Little, Brown Book Group.

Hunter, M. R., Gillespie, B. W., & Chen, S. Y. P. (2019). Urban nature experiences reduce stress in the context of daily life based on salivary biomarkers. *Frontiers in Psychology*, *10*, 722.

Pink, D. H. (2018). *When: The scientific secrets of perfect timing.* New York: Riverhead Books.

Tippett, K. (2016). *Becoming wise: An inquiry into the mystery and art of living.* New York: Penguin Press.

Watts, Alan. (1977). *The essence of Alan Watts.* Millbrae, CA: Celestial Arts.

Wilson, T. D., Reinhard, D. A., Westgate, E. C., Gilbert, D. T., Ellerbeck, N., Hahn, C., & Shaked, A. (2014). Just think: The challenges of the disengaged mind. *Science*, *345*(6192), 75–77.

9 CE-CERT Echoes: Creating Synergy Between the CE-CERT Skills

Live the questions now. Perhaps you will then gradually, without noticing it, live along some distant day into the answer.

Rainer Maria Rilke (n.d.)

As I write this chapter, I experience the very emotion that is the topic of this third act: I have a feeling of returning home. I feel very reflective about the ground that we have covered, all those concepts, skills, and citations. I hope you can create that feeling of returning home with the elixir, even if just for a moment. We have covered a lot of ground, a lot of practices. I believe that these concepts have defined a map. But, alas, the map is not the terrain. Understanding a concept is not equivalent to implementing it skillfully. As the accidental philosopher Mike Tyson put it, "Everybody has a plan until they get punched in the mouth" (quoted by Berardino, 2012).

I have described each of the five skills as just that—skills. But they also could be viewed as practices. Implementing these practices becomes the project of a career. Viewing the skills this way—as something we will get better at over our career—again draws a sharp distinction between CE-CERT and the common wisdom about the progression of burnout. I am conjuring a vision of an increasing sense of professional well-being over your career, rather than burning out. Take a moment to consider the possibility that instead of your energy and motivation for your work degrading a little more each year (day?), you become increasingly skillful at "consciously managing autonomic dysregulation".

There are several themes that echo across the skill domains. CE-CERT is a synthetic model, meaning that it is comprised of concepts and skills from many different empirical and theoretical sources. In synthesizing these concepts, there is a significant amount of crossover from one concept to another. That means that elements of the concepts relate to each other and overlap. But my interest here is not in how the model is conceptualized, but rather, my interest is in a functional reality: these "overlaps" create a transactional relationship in which skill in one domain facilitates another skill domain. I have divided the skills into five domains for heuristic purposes, but there is nothing real about that. Rather, as you begin incorporating this model, it will feel more like a unified practice as opposed to five separate skills.

CE-CERT Echo #1: Cognitive Breathing

All five of the CE-CERT skill domains facilitate the cognitive breath. Each skill supports either the inbreath, the outbreath, or the movement from one to the other. The first skill, experiential engagement, facilitates the taking of a full inbreath. Willingness to engage experience, whether pleasant or unpleasant, involves opening a "soft front" and breathing in fully whatever feelings may come up. Engaging those experiences—breathing in fully—allow us also to breath out fully. The analogy is that if we avoid unpleasant experience or dampen down our feelings, we are taking only a shallow cognitive breath. Or sometimes, through avoidance we are even holding our breath.

Reducing rumination skills support a full outbreath. When we ruminate about stressful situations, we are continuing the inbreath—we remain in fight or flight as if the threat were in the here-and-now. When we release those ruminative images and the resulting feelings, however, we remind ourselves to stop the inbreath so we can exhale into the present.

The conscious narrative allows the energy of the cognitive breath to move through us—both the inbreath and the outbreath. The antecedent narrative, "I am open to the experiences of this day..."; "I am willing to have my heart broken..." supports a full inhalation. As do the concurrent narratives, "I am willing to experience this difficult thing..."; "This stress is preparing me to engage this situation...". All these narratives facilitate opening to a full inbreath. The consolidation narrative allows the exhalation. These after-the-stress reflections situate the stress event in the past so we can exhale: "Now that the difficult situation is over, what can I learn from it?"

The last two skill domains, reducing emotional labor and parasympathetic recovery, focus on the outbreath. These two skills are about creating more ease or finding space within the day for moments of recovery. The more successful we are at increasing the sense of effortlessness, the easier it becomes to exhale, at least for a moment. And the more often we find that zone of emotional ease, the more willing we will be to engage the intensity when circumstances become difficult again.

Understanding the waves of stress as a *process*—cognitively breathing in and out—allows us to notice these vacillations better. We learn to trust the breath.

CE-CERT Echo #2: Stabilizing Swings from Intrusive Thoughts to Avoidance

An important echo occurs through the three skill domains experiential engagement, reducing rumination, and conscious narrative. This echoing dynamic precisely targets one of the central features of secondary traumatic stress: fluctuations between intrusive thoughts and avoidance. That is, people who are experiencing post-traumatic symptoms, whether from primary or secondary trauma, often swing between these two undesirable poles. Intrusive thoughts are a well-known feature of PTSD. Because these thoughts and images are unwelcome and are distressing, the person experiencing them is very likely to begin avoiding things or situations that may "trigger" them. But, as we have thoroughly established by now, avoidance cannot eliminate unwelcome thoughts or feelings. It is only a matter of *when* and *how* suppressed psychic energy will express itself in the form of an intrusive thought. And once we start avoiding, the stage is set for the swings from one extreme—avoidance—to the other—intrusive thoughts.

As we established in Chapter 2, experiential engagement—and the skills that bring about engagement—is the direct antidote to avoidance. If we engage a situation, we are obviously not avoiding it. The reducing rumination skills directly target the reduction of the intrusive thoughts. If we successfully reduce the ruminative thought, it isn't intruding any longer. Employing these two skills in tandem drains the energy that ricochets between suppressing the energy on the one hand and experiencing it intrusively on the other.

As the echo between experiential engagement and rumination reduction reduces the energy in this self-perpetuating system of ricochets, the anchor for our emotion regulation is the narrative context in which we place it. The whole energy system calms down when we are able to tell its story, both in real time and in reflection (consolidation narrative).

That is a rather complex set of concepts! But really, it is a rather simple case of how the skill domains organically operate. We don't have to direct the skills to work together; they naturally do. These complex concepts get much clearer when set within a case example. The first scenario is as it actually happened. The second is created to illustrate the application of the CE-CERT skills:

A child therapist is seeing a six-year-old boy in treatment. This boy was present when his younger brother was found in the grandmother's swimming pool immediately after the four-year-old had drown. He was brought into treatment by his mother. Understandably, both the mother and the six-year-old were experiencing profound trauma symptoms.

In the initial session, the therapist met alone with the mother. During this session, the mother described the trauma scenario in detail. The amount of secondary trauma exposure that the therapist experienced from the vivid scenario and intensity of feelings of the mother was profound. During the session—I'm focusing on the therapist—the therapist was calm and supportive. But inwardly, the therapist was suppressing strong and nearly overwhelming feelings of horror at this trauma scene. Afterward, the therapist talked to her supervisor and described the trauma scene but did so while holding herself distant from her feelings. When asked by her supervisor, she reported that she was doing fine and did not report—or experience—any strong reaction.

Later that night, while at home with her husband, the therapist began having images of this trauma scene intrude into her activities. Whenever that happened, she would push the thoughts away and try to focus on social apps or on a television show. She awoke in the middle of a night's sleep, and her thoughts immediately went to the trauma scene. In subsequent days she bounced from avoiding—and denying—any unusual level of feeling from exposure to this trauma story, only to be interrupted by unwelcome imagining of the scene. Her overall level of anxiety grew, and she began to experience dread at the thought of meeting again with this six-year-old and his mother for their scheduled session.

Now let's imagine the same set of circumstances with the CE-CERT skills applied. During the secondary exposure as the mother recounts this horrible scene, the therapist makes occasional "visits to herself". She notes that—although her job is to bear witness to this woman's trauma—she is also very disturbed to be brought onto this scene and the profound feelings that it elicits. She maintains her professional presence throughout the session, but at one point she looks into the eyes of the mother and, with tears in her eyes resulting from her own experienced sadness, says to her, "I am so sad that you have to go through this...". Although necessarily holding back a considerable amount of strong feelings, she acknowledges to herself that she is deeply affected by the images of this scene, and that debriefing those feelings will be important.

As soon after the session as possible, the therapist seeks out a trusted colleague. She tells her colleague that she has experienced an intense clinical session that she would like to debrief. She and her co-worker have established a relationship that allows them to provide this consultation to each other reciprocally. During this consultation, she explores and experiences all of her feelings about the witness she has just born. She describes feeling horror and profound sadness. She is visibly upset during this debrief but—and you will recognize why I accentuate this point—she is not overwhelmed. She is experiencing strong feelings, but she maintains confidence that she will not be swamped by those feelings.

During the evening, during moments of inactivity, she begins having images of the trauma scene. Note: these images will likely be less intense than those in the first scenario because they have been substantially depotentiated by the experience and expression of her feelings earlier in the day. As those images begin to intrude, she notes that she is beginning to ruminate about the session and the trauma event. Noting that these thoughts are intruding, she realizes that she needs a more absorbing activity than social media or a TV show. She phones her mother—something she has intended to do for several days—and engages in a 20-minute conversation. This has the twin advantages of holding her attention fully and helps her feel connected with another person. The images are less frequent and intense after this phone call. For the rest of the evening, if the images reappear all she needs to do is note them and remind herself to let them pass as she refocuses on the activity in which she is engaged.

Her emerging—and consciously cultivated—narrative also helps quiet her secondary trauma. Before the day, she opens to the experience of having her heart broken. Her narrative is that—although painful, she is willing to feel emotions of sadness. Her concurrent narrative is one that supports "I know what to do here", which prevents her from being overwhelmed. "I can't change the tragedy that occurred, and I don't have to. My role is to be courageous enough to bear witness to this mother's profound grief". Her consolidation narrative develops as she reflects on the growing knowledge of how she will handle this. Combined, these narrative themes support her emotional regulation. She has stepped out of the cycle of intrusive thoughts followed by periods of avoidance.

CE-CERT Echo #3: Allowing the Energy to Move Through

The ultimate goal of the CE-CERT skills is to allow the energy that arises from stress to complete its natural energy cycle. Secondary traumatic stress is the result of interrupting the natural rise and fall of the stress response. Allowing the energy of the "stress wave" to move through us rather than getting stuck within is the target.

Experiential engagement skills allow us to fully experience emotion so that the energy can be expressed and then naturally expended. Ruminations are the result of our mind holding on to a stressor rather than allowing it to move through. We are stuck in an earlier moment in time—when the stress event occurred—rather than being in the current moment. With each rumination, we rekindle the fight-or-flight experience and add fuel to it rather than allowing it to naturally recede. Therefore, as we become proficient at reducing unwanted ruminations, we are allowing the natural energy to move rather than be held and recycled in the default mode network.

The narratives that we intentionally cultivate serve either to open us to the natural rise of the stress response ("I am willing to have my heart broken today"; "This stress is signaling me to be ready to effectively engage this situation"), or they serve to help the response come to resolution ("It is over now, I can let it go"; "I know how to handle that situation next time I encounter it"). In short, the narratives that we are consciously cultivating are those that allow the energy to naturally rise and that allow it naturally to fade.

Reducing the amount of emotional labor in our work facilitates the movement of stress energy, but also confers the benefit of reducing the amount of negative stress energy in the system. When our job begins to feel less threatening, we are, in effect, relaxing from a clenched, defensive position. When we maintain an expectation of negative experience, we actually *create* it in the sense of dread. When we expect our work to be easier, we ease into a relaxed psychological position that allows the energy to simply take its course. Sometimes that energy is actually a positive energy that we hadn't noticed before because of our negative anticipation. When the energy is from a stress event, we are actually reducing the amount of stress energy in the system—the stress that we added unnecessarily in the form of emotional effort and anticipatory dread.

And finally, the purpose of the parasympathetic recovery skill domain is recovery. Recovery is, of course, the relinquishment of our stress energy. This skill domain, parasympathetic recovery, focuses on creating moments of space that allow the stress waves to finish rather than to accumulate within your body. Sympathetic response and parasympathetic recovery are precisely the energy referred to in the phrase "allowing the energy to move through". The sympathetic response is the accumulation of the energy, and parasympathetic recovery is the discharge of that same energy. One side of the skill set is allowing the energy with openness, and the other side allows and facilitates the completion of the energy cycle.

CE-CERT Echo #4: Transactional Relationship Between the Skill Domains

Each CE-CERT skill can be conceptualized as a muscle that can be developed and strengthened. But movement requires not a single strong muscle, but a set of muscles working in coordination. And likewise, cognitive breathing is produced by the way that all of the CE-CERT skill domains work together. Reducing emotional labor, for example, becomes much easier if we have cultivated narratives that allow us to anticipate the workday without a sense of dread. These transactional relationships operate bi-directionally, and each skill domain adds energy to every other skill domain.

As an example, consider the first skill we discussed—experiential engagement: If I fully engage a stress event, the energy of the event expends itself. As discussed in Chapter 2, the fever spikes within a discrete time rather than becoming a slow burning, low-grade fever. Because allowing the energy to run its natural course without interruption allows the stress energy to deplete itself, the recollection of the event is less energized. That makes it less likely that I will experience intrusive ruminations of the event during the evening at home. In other words, ruminations are the result of suppressing or dampening down the psychic energy of the stress event. That is one direction of the transaction: full engagement of emotions reduces the frequency and intensity of ruminations. The other direction of the transaction is that if I possess a sense of efficacy that I can manage ruminations, it is easier for me to open up to full engagement of intense experiences. Most of us would be quite willing to tolerate these experiences for the few minutes of the actual experience. Our avoidance stems from the fear of—and past experience of—having them change our emotional state for hours afterwards and having ruminations about them well into the evening. When we become skillful at "leaving the moment in the moment", it becomes easier to open to the experience in the first place.

There are some obvious synergies between our willingness to engage intense experience and the narratives that we tell ourselves. In Chapter 4, I discussed the importance of antecedent narratives that help create willingness to open up to experience (e.g., "I am willing to feel whatever comes up in my work today..." or "This work is deeply important to me..."). Our concurrent narratives help us stay engaged in difficult moments ("I am willing to feel this..."; "This stress is telling me to lean in and deal with this..."). And, certainly, cultivating a consolidation narrative that makes all of this seem worthwhile primes our willingness to engage difficult things again.

The transactional relationship between experiential willingness and reducing emotional labor can be easily illustrated by contrasting two simple examples: In the first, you engaged an experience with a client who was in a suicidal crisis. After the session is over, you feel emotionally exhausted. Throughout the experience you were afraid you were mishandling the situation, and terrified that if you made an error the client could die, and you could be left with the liability for your error. In other words, your emotional labor load is very heavy.

In the second example, you engage the deep feelings of despondency in the client and their suffering over the events that provoked this crisis. You are able to access deep compassion for this person and are able to successfully communicate that caring. You have dealt with many clients who have an elevated risk for suicide and are confident that you know appropriate protocols for assessing and intervening in cases of suicidal ideation. After the session, you feel deeply moved by the emotional connection that you were able to have with this person.

To understand the organic relationship between experiential willingness and emotional labor, simply compare these two case scenarios.

After having each of these experiences, how willing are you likely to be to engage these situations with a "soft front" in the future? If you sometimes tend toward avoidance, how much of that tendency might derive from feeling overwhelmed because you don't know what to do in this particular situation? How much of your unwillingness might derive from the fact that in such situations, you are in survival mode and therefore are not able to experience deep compassion for the client? Or how much unwillingness derives from the mistaken idea that you don't want to experience compassion for this client because you might be drawn into despondency yourself?

And lastly, we will be more willing to engage intense experiences if we also know that we will have opportunities to "breathe" during the day. I described experiential engagement as the inbreath—being willing to open up to the full breath of experience. I can't take one, eight-hour inbreath each day—work can't all be inbreath or breath-holding. My willingness to open to a difficult, aversive situation hinges directly upon my confidence—and narrative—that immediately after the inbreath, I can take the outbreath. Again, the work–life balance worldview makes us more *unwilling* to engage experiences because it feels like we must engage them for the whole day. But when we get enough airspace between the hotspots of our day, the fire—your energy and motivation—can burn fully.

I could take each skill domain and illustrate similarly the way one proficiency echoes off from another. But by now, you get the point. When we have developed adeptness at one skill, the others are actually facilitated by mastery in the other domains. These muscles will work together.

CE-CERT Echo #5: Expertise

I have already cited research demonstrating something that you already suspected: secondary traumatic stress is correlated with the amount of exposure one has to trauma cases. But—as I pointed out in the first chapter, this relationship is not a directly causal one. Secondary trauma is not caused by exposure *unless there is a specific mediating variable: the therapist feels helpless and overwhelmed.*

This factor is easy to demonstrate on its face: a particular situation that results in secondary traumatic stress to one therapist does not to another therapist. One therapist may even describe the situation as rewarding. The research literature is replete with studies defining the myriad risk factors for secondary trauma: organizational factors, personal history, years of experience. Personal and even physiological difference between individual therapists certainly play a role. But I want to focus on one of the most profound differences between those who will experience secondary traumatic stress and those who will not: level of expertise. Expertise in anything—whether tennis or painting portraits or doing psychotherapy—is some combination of native ability and focused practice. We can't do anything to influence native ability, but expertise can be attained. CE-CERT is predicated on the fact that expertise in the ability to "consciously control autonomic dysregulation" can be developed with focused effort.

I have worked alongside a number of trauma therapists who intuitively practice all of the CE-CERT skills. Most of them couldn't identify what they are doing or how they do it; they just naturally have this ability. But most of us aren't that way—we are negatively affected in our work as trauma therapists in various ways. I risk being accused of "blaming the victim" by suggesting that this distress—or secondary traumatic stress—calls for greater expertise. But I find within that insight lies a great margin of hopefulness. Another through line of CE-CERT is the substitution of active responses for passive responses. If we believe that we are victims of the buffeting of the trauma-exposed environment in which we work, this leads to a passive response. If, on the other hand, our response to trauma exposure is viewed as its own kind of expertise, this generates an active response. Even more so if we have a map for what this active response should be—focusing on developing specific skills.

An ancient Sufi prayer wished for you to "overcome any bitterness that may have come because you were not up to the magnitude of the pain that was entrusted to you" (Brach, 2003). That ancient thought inserts a brand-new idea within the secondary response: that we should—and can—develop an expertise that equals the difficulty of the trauma work that we are doing.

You possess a certain expertise gained from your graduate training and experience. Perhaps you have acquired expertise on treating children who have experienced trauma. Perhaps you have acquired expertise on strategies for supporting distress tolerance in your clients. But the interventional models for which you have developed expertise all began with the second chapter of their respective treatment manuals. They forgot—or presumed—that you already have the first chapter. The first chapter—that your clinical instructors presumed you had—is how to remain emotionally regulated in your interaction with the client. The proponents of the intervention models presuppose that you will implement their defined protocols without becoming reactive to your client. And they presuppose that you will not experience too much distress, so you will remain in your job long enough to acquire expertise in the model via training, reading, and supervision. To do all that they presuppose requires its own skill set. Remaining in your job for a long and satisfying career requires "a particular set of skills". CE-CERT specifically articulates those unarticulated prerequisite skills.

Echoing throughout the CE-CERT skills is that the pleasure of your job resides only within your window of tolerance. That is when you feel good in your role as a therapist. That is when you are able to experience the very compassion that is prerequisite to the success of any treatment approach. All of us may differ in how reactive our emotion regulation system is, and how quickly it recovers. But the central aim of CE-CERT is to identify skills that allow you to develop a kind of expertise that was likely not discussed nor explicitly supervised during your graduate training. And this expertise is an essential precondition to the kind of expertise that defines the craftwork of trauma treatment.

Conclusion

Each day of trauma work is, in itself, a tale told in three acts—if we are telling our story properly, that is. The first act begins each day as we decide whether we will accept the challenge of the quest. Will we—rather than girding our loins for battle—ungird ourselves and open to whatever heartaches and rewards that that day will offer? Every day we make the decision. Sometimes the challenge is declined. We are, after all, imperfect humans. But sometimes we accept the challenge with courage.

Each day is filled with the contests between us and whatever the stress events of that day happen to be. Sometimes, those challenges are defined more in the stuff of bureaucratic hoop-jumping than anything else. But sometimes the challenges are intense—they are played out at the level of life-and-death struggles for some of our clients. And we are in the position of attempting to bend the trajectory of that struggle. Sometimes we are unable to. But sometimes we do. Some days the challenges are something else entirely—invitations to open fully to the simple pleasures of seeing our clients get better. Of laughing in the hallway with a colleague, who is one of a select few who understands the challenges we deal with each day.

Each day we come home with a little more of the special elixir—a little more knowledge. Maybe the new knowledge is just a simple technique that worked with a specific client in a specific way. Or maybe it is an entirely new model in how to intervene with clients. Or maybe today was an unremarkable day in which we quietly got a little better at the things we already knew how to do pretty well.

And—maybe—today we got a little better at maintaining our own emotional window of tolerance. Perhaps we had a success at opening up to something that has, heretofore, been too aversive. Maybe we experienced a success in allowing an intense event to quickly pass through us rather than ruining our whole day. Maybe we figuratively wrote another paragraph in our narrative called "why this work matters". We had the experience of pure compassion for a difficult client. We had a day in which there was perfect balance between absolute intensity, followed by moments of supreme calm. And also, we had some days in which we realized that none of that happened. And tomorrow, you will try to do something a little different. Maybe you are going to try to learn how to make this a little easier.

I don't know you, the reader of this book, but I feel a kindredship with you. This connection is born of the fact that we labor together in the helping professions. It is part of my career-sustaining narrative that I have chosen a *helping* profession. What better profession is there than that? This work can feel very solitary at times, but we helping professionals are legion. You aren't doing this alone.

Some time ago, I was preparing to present at a large gathering of child protection workers. I sat in the hallway of a huge convention center as the breakout sessions simultaneously ended. As the attendees left their respective training sessions and walked out of the meetings rooms to gather in the large central conference center, I became acutely aware of the thundering of thousands of footsteps. It sounded like an army. It *was* an army—an army of trained personnel who were devoting their efforts to protecting children from abuse. It was thrilling to me to realize that this army existed. But it was sad to me that on normal days, each of them labored in small teams, and in the isolation of their own office, and were unaware they were part of this army. Not only is this an army, but no one can argue that this army isn't on the side of the angels. I hope that is woven into your career narrative.

I end with my sincere hope for you—as a fellow helping professional working to reduce the suffering of those who have experienced trauma:

I wish you the strength to hold the suffering that the world wishes to ignore.
Hold it gently, so that you may also let it go.
This willingness to hold the suffering of others will require that you pay particular attention to your own well-being. May you succeed in doing so.
May you discover joy in the sure knowledge that your vocation exists singularly to support the well-being of another human being. There is no higher calling.

References

Berardino, M. (November 9, 2012). Mike Tyson explains one of his most famous quotes. Retrieved from https://www.sun-sentinel.com/sports/fl-xpm-2012-11-09-sfl-mike-tyson-explains-one-of-his-most-famous-quotes-20121109-story.html.

Brach, T. (2003). *Radical acceptance: Embracing your life with the heart of a Buddha*. New York: Bantam Books.

Rilke, R. M. (n.d.). Letters to a young poet. Retrieved from http://www.columbia.edu/~ey2172/rilke.html.

Index

workload 129–30
worrying *see* rumination

YAVIS (young, attractive, verbal,
   intelligent, and successful)
   clients 132

yogic breathing 72

Zen Cowboy ethic 157
Zen monks 63

Made in the USA
Monee, IL
10 November 2022

17485452R00114